MCK

SS

INTERIM SITE   x398

Picar...
Celt...   SO-ASG-015

x398
P 58c
cop.1

3 1192 00017 6386

3

CELTIC TALES

Legends of Tall Warriors & Old Enchantments

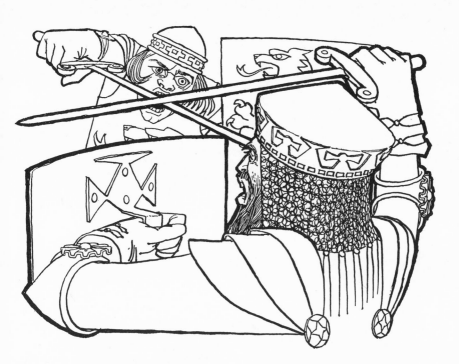

CELTIC TALES

Legends of Tall Warriors &
Old Enchantments

retold by
BARBARA LEONIE PICARD

illustrated by
JOHN G. GALSWORTHY

CRITERION BOOKS
NEW YORK

Manufactured in the United States of America

CONTENTS

5

PREFACE

WHEN I was choosing the stories for retelling in a previous book, *Tales of the British People*, I found it very hard to decide which two stories to include as examples of tales told by the Celtic settlers in the British Isles. The same problem faced me when selecting stories for the Irish and Welsh sections in *Hero Tales from the British Isles*. In both cases the difficulty arose through the necessity of having to choose only a few stories from such an abundance of fine Celtic material—there was so much which I could hardly bear to leave out. That is the reason for this book: to make a small collection of some of the good Celtic stories which I had to omit from the two previous volumes.

Once again, I have written brief notes about the stories and their backgrounds; and, as before, these notes are in no way necessary to the stories, which can be enjoyed without them. But I hope that a few readers, at least, will derive added pleasure and interest from the notes.

B. L. P.

THE CHILDREN OF LIR

Ancient Irish mythology is a record of the predominance of successive dynasties of gods, each dynasty being in turn attacked, defeated and succeeded by invading gods who arrived in Ireland from some mysterious place of origin. After conquest, the victors would often be harassed and vexed by the survivors of the defeated, who would be full of spite towards them and eager for vengeance. In this we may see a legendary record of the successive historic invasions of Ireland made by different peoples from over the sea, each of which would have brought with it its own gods; authentic invasions, all knowledge of which has been lost, save in these mythological accounts.

We know most about the last of these families of gods to reach Ireland, deities who were brought to that land by the Celtic invaders, and were known as the children, or people, of the goddess Dana. The people of Dana were said to have come down to Ireland from the sky in a cloud of mist one May Day and, after long and fierce fighting, to have defeated their divine predecessors, the Fomors.

These new gods were believed to be descended from Dana, the universal mother, goddess of the fruitful earth, whose husband was Bilé; and their first king was her son, Nuada of the Silver Hand, who was slain in battle against the Fomors and was later succeeded as ruler by Bov the Red.

One of the chief gods was the Dagda, who was a god of the earth and of the round of the year. When he played on his oaken harp, the seasons followed each other in their appointed order. He owned a cauldron from which all might receive food and from which no one was turned away unsatisfied. His wife was Boann, goddess of the River Boyne, and amongst his children were Bov the Red, his eldest son, who became king of the gods; Angus of the Birds, the god of love; Midir the Proud, the god of the underworld; and Brigit, the goddess of fire and the hearth.

In time, we are told, men came from over the sea to settle in Ireland—they too, like the people of Dana, were descended from gods, but, unlike them, they were mortal—and at their coming the people of Dana retired to secret places and homes far removed from the everyday life of the new inhabitants of Ireland. Some of them, like Manannan Mac Lir, the sea-god, departed to other lands, but many of them went to live in magnificent magical palaces in secluded spots, or inside hills. Yet they could pass unseen at their will through Ireland, and often they would concern themselves with the doings of mortals.

The story of The Children of Lir *begins in the days before men came to Ireland, when the people of Dana were supreme, and ends nine hundred years later, in Christian times. It is, of course, a Christian version of what must have been a much older story.*

★　★　★

In the old days when the gods and the children of the gods lived in Ireland, the people of the goddess Dana came together to choose a king from four of the great ones amongst them: Bov the Red, his brothers, Midir the Proud and Angus of the Birds, and Lir, father of Manannan the sea-god. After due discussion, their choice fell on Bov the Red. All the people of Dana approved this choice save Lir, who had thought to be chosen himself. And because he would not give his allegiance to Bov, he retired to his own home at the Hill of the White Field, in that place which is now the County Armagh; and there he remained, untroubled by Bov, who left him in peace and would suffer no one else to molest him, in spite of his defiance.

For many years things went thus, until one day, after an illness of three days, Lir's wife died and he was left sorrowing for her. When news of this reached Bov's court, he said, 'For all his grief, Lir will, in time, take another wife, for no man should live unwed, and when that day comes, it would please me greatly if he were to marry one of my foster-daughters, so that the breach between us might be healed at last.'

He sent to Lir with words of friendship, offering him whichever one of his foster-daughters he cared to have for his wife; and Lir, who also was glad that their enmity should be ended, set off from his home to Lough Derg on the Shannon, where Bov held his court. There he was welcomed kindly, and there at last he acknowledged Bov as king; and Bov made a great feast for him. Then, the next day, Bov took Lir to where his three foster-daughters, Aev, Eva and Alva, sat with their foster-mother, the queen, and he said to Lir, 'Take now your choice of them. Whichever one you wish shall be yours.'

Lir looked at the three maidens, and each one was as lovely as her sisters, so he said, 'All three are beautiful, but I will choose the eldest, since she is likely to be the wisest also.'

That very day Lir and Aev were married, and after the wedding feast she went with him to the Hill of the White Field. There in the house of Lir, in due time, twins were born to her, a daughter and a son, whom they named Finola and Aed. A year or two later she once again bore twins, two boys, whom they called Fiachra and Conn; but to Lir's great grief, she died at their birth. Lir mourned so deeply for the death of Aev, that it is said he would have died himself from sorrow, had he not had his four little children to take his mind from his grief.

When the news of Aev's death reached the court of Bov the Red, he and all his people raised three loud cries of lamentation for her. But when their mourning was ended, Bov said, 'This grief falls hardest on Lir; but let him comfort himself with another wife from my house.' And he sent to Lir, offering him his second foster-daughter, Eva.

Lir accepted, and when some little time was passed, Lir went again to the court of Bov and fetched Eva home to the Hill of the White Field.

Eva loved Lir's four young children and tended them with care, as though they had been her own; and indeed, so winning and so beautiful they were, all four, that not only their father and his household held them in great affection, but also Bov, who loved them almost as well as did Lir. Many times each year would Bov travel to the Hill of the White Field to see Lir's children; and many times a year would he have them at his court, and always, when the day for the ending of their visit was come, he was loath to part from them.

But in time, seeing how everyone doted on her sister's children, Eva's love for them grew cold and jealousy took its place: yet this she succeeded in hiding. That she might not see the loving looks that others cast on the children, and that she might not have the children themselves ever before her eyes, she feigned an illness and took to her bed, where she remained for many months. Yet her solitude did not cure her jealousy, but only made it stronger, for she did naught all day but lie and imagine herself neglected and slighted, until at last she fell to hating the children. When finally, after a year had passed, she could bear the thought of them no longer, she rose from her bed and ordered her chariot to be made ready to carry her and the children to the court of Bov, as so often in the past.

But when Finola saw the strange, brooding look in her stepmother's eyes, she knew that some dreadful fate awaited her and her brothers; yet so strong was her destiny upon her that she did nothing to prevent it, but went with Eva, along with Fiachra and Conn and Aed.

When they had travelled a certain distance from the Hill of the White Field, Eva ordered the chariot to stop. Then she called to her servants and bid them kill the children. 'For,' she said, 'their father cares nothing for me and neglects me. All his love is for his children, he has none left to spare for his wife.'

With horror the servants heard her command and refused to obey. 'It is a fearful deed that you have bidden us perform, and surely evil will come upon you for it,' they said.

In anger she snatched a sword from one of her men, and would have slain the children with her own hand: but she could not bring herself to do it. So she entered the chariot again and ordered the charioteer to drive on.

On the shore of Lake Darvra—now Lough Derryvaragh in West Meath—she ordered the chariot to stop and the horses to be unyoked. Then she gathered the four children about her and went with them to the edge of the lake. There she bade them take off their clothes and bathe, to refresh themselves after the journey.

Now, Eva had powers of sorcery, and as soon as the children had entered the water, she struck them one by one with a wand and changed them into four beautiful swans with feathers as white as snow, and she spoke their fate in a verse:

> On lonely Lake Darvra, children of Lir,
> Let you cry with the wildfowl over the mere;
> For Lir himself and all who love you well,
> Shall never recall my lasting spell.

With terror the four swans heard her, and Finola said, 'This is a cruel deed that you have done, stepmother, and all unmerited. Yet though you may not love us, there are many who do, and their power is greater than yours. In the end, your fate shall be worse than ours.' Then,

as the full horror of their plight came to her mind, she said, 'Tell us, stepmother, how long must we remain as swans? Is there any hope at all left to us?'

'It would have been better for you had you not asked me that question,' said Eva, 'for the answer can bring you naught but grief. Yet since you have asked, you shall have the answer. Three hundred years shall you stay here on Lake Darvra; three hundred years shall you swim on the stormy Sea of Moyle; and three hundred years shall you pass on the Isle of Glora, in the Western Sea. In the shape of swans you must remain until the man of the North shall take as his wife the woman of the South, and until you hear the sound of the bell that shall proclaim to you that the old gods are no more and a new faith is come to Ireland.'

Then, as Eva realized fully what she had done, she repented; but it was too late, for she had no power to undo her spell. Yet she did what she could for her stepchildren. 'You shall keep your speech,' she promised, 'and your understanding. In all things you shall be as you

13

were, save only in your shape. You can converse with those who love you, and the songs which you will sing shall be sweeter than any music and they shall have the gift of bringing comfort and rest to all who hear them.' Then she ordered the horses to be yoked to the chariot and she drove on to the court of Bov, leaving the four white swans on Lake Darvra.

When Bov saw that she had come to him alone, he was disappointed and asked her where the children were.

'They are at home,' she answered.

'Why did you not bring them with you, as you have ever done?'

'Because Lir no longer trusts you. He thinks you mean to harm his children.'

Bov was astonished and greatly perturbed at this and he asked, 'How can Lir mistrust me? I love his children as I love my own.' And he sent messengers northwards to the Hill of the White Field, to ask Lir concerning the matter.

Lir could not understand Bov's message and could only ask, 'Have the children not reached Lough Derg with Eva?'

'She came alone, and she told the king that you would not permit them to go with her,' he was answered.

Lir knew then that some misfortune had come upon his beloved children, and immediately he set out for Bov's court. As he passed by Lake Darvra, Finola and her brothers saw him and swam hastily towards the shore. 'It is our father,' they cried to each other.

When Lir heard the swans speaking, he was greatly astonished, and he stopped and asked them, 'Who are you that speak like the people of Dana?'

'We are your four children, Lir, changed into this shape through the jealousy of our stepmother.'

Lir and his followers raised three cries of lamentation at Finola's words; and when she told him how they were doomed to remain as swans for nine hundred years, his grief knew no bounds. 'At least, dearest children, come home with me to the Hill of the White Field, where you may dwell amongst those who love you,' he said.

'Alas, my father, here on Lake Darvra we must remain for three hundred years,' they answered.

Lir and his followers wept; but Finola said, 'Stay here with us for

14

tonight and we shall sing our songs to you. They will charm away
your grief and bring you sweet sleep.'

So that night Lir and his people remained on the shore of the lake,
and Finola and Aed, Fiachra and Conn, talked with them and sang to
them; so that their hearts were comforted and they fell into a gentle
sleep, even as Eva had foretold.

In the morning Lir bade his children farewell and drove on to
Lough Derg. There he told Bov of Eva's treachery; and Bov's grief
matched his own. Bov turned to his foster-daughter and saw from the
look in her eyes that Lir spoke the truth. 'Your fate shall be worse by
far than theirs,' he said, 'for their sorrow—long though it may last—
shall have an end. Yours shall endure for ever.' He looked at her in
wrath, so that she shrank from him. 'I charge you, Eva, tell me what
shape or form in all the world it is, that you most dread to be.'

And because he had laid it upon her to tell the truth, cowering before
him, she spoke it. 'Of all things, I fear most to be a demon of the air.'

Thereupon Bov struck her with his wand and she became a demon of
the air. She spread her wings wide, and with a terrible cry she rose upwards into the air and flew away through the clouds. And from that
day to this, Eva has remained a demon of the air, forever flying; and
so she shall remain until the end of time.

Then Bov the Red and Lir and their folk went and encamped on the
shore of Lake Darvra, and there they built homes for themselves, so
that they might always be near to Finola and her brothers. During the
day they all talked together merrily, and at night the four swans sang
their sweet songs, so that all who heard them were eased of affliction
and pain and fell into a peaceful sleep from which they awoke refreshed
and joyful.

And so in this way, close to those who loved them, the children of
Lir passed three hundred years as pleasantly and as contentedly as
though they had been living at the Hill of the White Field. But at the
end of that time, with sadness Finola said to her brothers, 'We must now
leave this happy place and go to the Sea of Moyle where we shall be
lonely and sorrowful.'

With great grief they bade their father and their friends farewell and
sang to them for the last time. Then, spreading their white wings, they
rose up into the air and flew to the north-east, away towards the Sea

of Moyle which lies between Ireland and Scotland; and long did the people of Dana lament their loss.

Cold and lonely and often hungry, the children of Lir passed the days of their first year on the stormy Sea of Moyle, keeping ever close together for comfort until one winter evening when a great tempest blew up. Seeing the black, threatening clouds as they gathered in the sky, Finola grew afraid and said to her brothers, 'Surely tonight will bring such a storm as we have never seen before. I fear that in the darkness we shall be separated. Let us agree now on a place of meeting where we can go when the storm has died down.'

'That is wisely spoken, dear sister,' they said. 'Let us all meet again on the rock of Carricknarone, for we know that place well.'

At midnight the wind struck the sea with violence; huge waves towered above the four swans; thunder roared and lightning flashed; and, as Finola had foreseen, in the darkness they were parted and scattered, tossed everywhere by the wind and the waves, so that they barely came through the night with their lives.

By morning the tempest had passed and the sea was calm, and Finola swam quickly to Carricknarone, eager to meet Aed, Fiachra and Conn. But she came to the rock to find it deserted, and nowhere around could she see any sign of her brothers. She waited, afraid and sorrowing, and sang a sad chant for them; then she looked up and saw, afar off, Conn coming towards the rock, drooping and weary. Hardly had they greeted each other joyfully when Fiachra came in sight, so weak that he could hardly reach the rock, and so weary that he could not speak to them. Then Aed rejoined his sister and his brothers, and rejoicing, Finola took Fiachra and Conn, one under each of her wings, while Aed she placed beneath the feathers of her breast; and so they huddled together, comforting one another.

'Alas, dear brothers,' said Finola, 'there will be many nights like last night, before we leave the Sea of Moyle.' And she spoke truly.

Upon the Sea of Moyle they suffered much hardship and pain; but all things pass, and at length there came a day when they had lived on the Sea of Moyle for three hundred years.

'Tomorrow, dear brothers,' said Finola, 'we must leave here. It is time for us to go to the Isle of Glora in the Western Sea.'

So they spread their wings and rose into the air and flew westwards.

On the way they passed over the Hill of the White Field and there they alighted, where their father's home had been. But the house had long since crumbled and vanished; its stones lay under the turf; nettles and coarse grass grew in the ruins of the hall, and cold winds blew over it.

The four swans gave three long, sad cries of lamentation, and sang a song for all the days of the past and the friends who were gone; then they flew on towards the Isle of Glora, off the Connaught coast, where they alighted on a small lake.

Here they lived, singing their songs; and the birds from the mainland, hearing their sweet voices, flew over the water to them and stayed to listen, until the island came to be the home of countless birds, and the lake itself became known as the Lake of Birds, so many were always gathered there.

And so the years went by until three hundred had gone, and Patrick the Christian came to Ireland, telling the people of a new faith, preaching and baptizing and building churches, up and down the country. Among his followers was a man named Kemoc, who came one day to the Isle of Glora and built a little church there.

One morning the children of Lir heard a strange sound, such as they had never heard before—the sound of the bell of Kemoc's church ringing for matins. And they were afraid, for they did not know what it was. Then Finola remembered Eva's words. 'Do not fear, my brothers,' she said. 'It is the sound of the bell of the new faith and it means that our sufferings are almost over and our stepmother's enchantment will soon be broken, even as she herself said.'

At her words they feared no longer, but listened to the bell until it ceased, and then they sang a song of their own. Kemoc heard it from his little church and, marvelling, came out to see. He walked down to the lakeside and spoke to them, and they told him that they were the children of Lir.

'I have heard the story of your long sorrow,' he said. 'But now your sufferings are over. Come with me, for it is here that your enchantment is destined to end.'

So they went with Kemoc and lived with him in his house, in peace and quietness; and Kemoc was glad to have them with him. But part of Eve's spell was yet unfulfilled: the marriage of a man of the North with a woman from the South.

Now, at that time the king of Connaught, in the north-west of Ireland, was named Largnen, and he was betrothed to Decca, daughter of the king of Munster, in the south. Decca had heard of the four swans who lived at the Lake of Birds in her husband's kingdom, and who sang so sweetly, and on her wedding day she demanded them of Largnen. But Largnen considered Kemoc a good and holy man, and he did not wish to offend him. Yet when Decca threatened to return to her father in Munster, he gave way to her demands, and sent to Kemoc, bidding him give up the swans to the queen. This Kemoc refused to do, and Largnen, angered by his refusal, grew as determined as Decca, and went himself to Kemoc's house to fetch the swans. Kemoc, seeing him coming, hid them in his little church; but Largnen broke open the door and dragged them out.

Yet Largnen had gone no more than a short way from the church when the swan-feathers fell from the children of Lir; and it was not four swans that Largnen was taking to the queen, but an old, old woman and three old, old men, all frail and bony and wrinkled.

Largnen was so fearful that he fled from the place; but Kemoc stayed beside them and baptized them, for he saw that they had not long to live.

'Good Kemoc,' said Finola, 'we have not been unhappy with you, and we shall be sorry to leave you. When we are dead, bury us together in one grave. Even as so often, when we were swans, I sheltered my brothers under my wings and under the feathers of my breast, so let us be in our grave. Place Conn at my right side, Fiachra at my left, and Aed before my face.'

'It shall be so,' promised Kemoc.

Then, quietly and peacefully, the children of Lir died; and, as he had promised, Kemoc laid them in one wide grave, with a green mound above them and a stone with their names engraved on it.

*　*　*

The Children of Lir *is one of 'The Three Sorrows of Storytelling'. The other two are* The Quest of the Sons of Turenn *and the tragic tale of* Deirdre and the Sons of Usna.

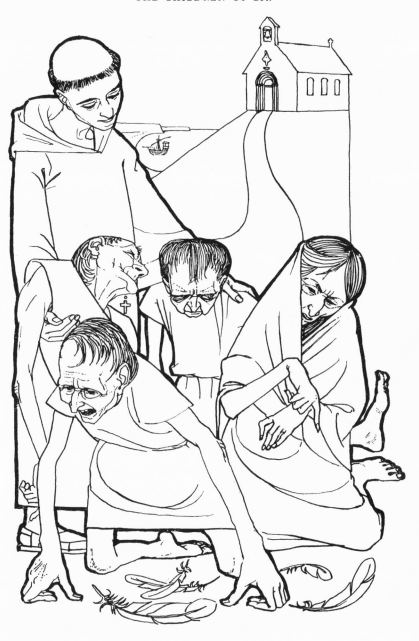

Largnen, son of Colman, king of Connaught, and his wife Decca, daughter of King Finnin of Munster, were real historical figures who lived in the seventh century.

2

THE ADVENTURES OF MANAWYDDAN

The ancient peoples of Ireland and of Britain were two branches of the same Celtic race. Their gods were probably once the same gods, but in their separate countries two differing mythologies evolved, just as the Welsh and Gaelic languages grew independently of each other, but from a common Celtic root. Our knowledge of the gods of ancient Britain is drawn mainly from Welsh sources, since the old traditions and beliefs survived longer in Wales than in England. But the stories from Irish mythology which have come down to us are far older than the remaining Welsh myths, and are therefore nearer to their original form. In the Welsh tales most of the deities have lost their godhead and become mere wonder-workers or mortal heroes, and are often only recognizable with difficulty. But in many of the Irish tales the gods are still gods, or, at the least, immortals of one kind or another.

The British gods can be roughly divided into two families: the children of Don and the children of Llyr. The family of the goddess Don—she is, of course, the same as the Irish earth-mother Dana—and her husband Beli were predominantly deities of the upper world: Arianrod, Gwydion, and their son, Lleu Llaw Gyffes, the sun-god; and the sky-god Lludd or Nudd—the Irish Nuada—who, as Lludd, had a temple on the site of St Paul's Cathedral and gave his name to Ludgate. The son of Nudd, Gwyn, the god of battle and the dead, once an important deity, was in early Christian times degraded to the status of an evil spirit of darkness, and later still was known throughout the Middle Ages as the sinister Gwyn ap Nudd, the king of the Welsh fairies. Of the family of Llyr, the most important were his giant son Bran, god of the underworld, Bran's sister Branwen, who was probably a goddess of beauty, and Manawyddan.

In this next story, Manawyddan, son of Llyr—here an ancient hero, but formerly a marine deity—is the Welsh form of Manannan Mac Lir, the Irish sea-god, half-brother to Finola, Aed, Conn and Fiachra of the previous story. It is a mediaeval Christian version of an ancient myth, and as we read it, we can occasionally catch echoes of a very much older tale.

The marriage of Branwen, sister of Bran, the king of Britain, to the king of Ireland, had caused a war between the two countries which had only ended when all the Irish warriors were dead and only seven of Bran's warriors were left alive. It is at this point that the adventures of Manawyddan begin. Caswallawn the usurper is the son of Beli, of the rival divine family of Don.

* * *

After Bran, the mighty king of Britain, had fallen fighting against the Irish, the seven warriors, who were all that remained of the huge army that had gone with him to Ireland, buried his head in London on the White Mount, facing towards France, so that it might for ever be a protection for Britain against enemies from over the sea.

Then the seven friends looked at one another sadly and made ready to part company; but Manawyddan, son of Llyr, Bran's brother, sighed and said, 'What will become of me? Every man in Britain, save only I, has a home and a shelter of his own. My home was at the court of my brother Bran: and now Bran is dead. And his son whom he left to guard his kingdom when he went to fight in Ireland is dead also, slain by the usurper Caswallawn, son of Beli, who now rules in Britain. In all this wide land there can be no resting-place for the brother of Bran.'

'Lord,' said young Pryderi, prince of Dyved, 'since the death of my father Pwyll, I have been ruler of Dyved, and Dyved is mine to do with as I will. You have ever been peaceable, not given to snatching lands or possessions for yourself, accept now as a gift the land of Dyved. It is a fair land and fruitful, and you will be rich in its possession. And if you wish, you may take for your wife my mother Rhiannon, for she is still young and has ever had great beauty.'

Manawyddan, much moved, said, 'May you one day be rewarded for your great friendship, Pryderi.' And together Manawyddan and Pryderi travelled to Dyved, in Wales.

In Narberth, the chief stronghold of Dyved, they were welcomed by Rhiannon and by Kicva, Pryderi's wife, and a great feast was made for Manawyddan. While Pryderi and Kicva delighted in each other's company after their long parting, it fell to the widowed Rhiannon to entertain the guest. Both she and Manawyddan liked the looks of each other, and soon they were deep in converse, as if they were old friends.

At the height of the feasting, Manawyddan broke off his talk with Rhiannon to call along the table to his host, 'I accept your offer, Pryderi.'

'Lord, I am very glad of it,' replied Pryderi.

'What offer is this, that you have made, my son?' asked Rhiannon.

'I have offered you as a wife to Manawyddan, son of Llyr, if it is pleasing to you both.'

Rhiannon smiled and looked at Manawyddan. 'It is pleasing to me,' she said.

'And to me,' said Manawyddan; and he and Rhiannon were married before the end of that same feasting.

So Manawyddan and Pryderi ruled in Dyved where all was happy and peaceful, and there was great love between them and Rhiannon and Kicva, and the four would never be parted at any time.

One evening their talk turned on the green hill which stood close by the castle of Narberth and of which it was said that no man might sit upon it without receiving a blow or a wound, or seeing a marvel. Now, it was this very same hill upon which Pwyll had been sitting when he had had his first glimpse of Rhiannon, so Pryderi said, 'The hill brought good fortune to my father, so this very day I shall sit upon it and see what befalls.'

'If you sit upon the hill, then I shall sit upon it with you, so that I may share your fate,' said Manawyddan.

'That fate shall be ours, too,' said their wives.

So together Manawyddan and Pryderi, Rhiannon and Kicva, went from the castle to the top of the hill, and a great number of their followers came with them and stood about the foot of the hill to see what would happen.

The four sat down upon the grassy crest of the hill and waited; and before many moments had passed, there was a sound of thunder rolling across the sky and a grey mist came about them, so thick that they could not even see each other. Then, as suddenly as it had come, the mist lifted and there were the four of them on the top of the hill; but their followers were nowhere in sight. And as they stood up and looked around them, they saw that the cattle and the flocks which had been grazing near the hill were gone; and gone, too, were the dwellings of the peasants that had been clustered about the walls of the castle: neither roof-thatch nor hearthstone of any one of them remained.

'This is indeed a marvel,' they said in amazement.

'The stronghold of Narberth, at least, still stands,' said Manawyddan. 'Let us go within and see what we shall find.'

They went through the gates and on into the hall, through the sleeping-places, the kitchens, the store-rooms and the women's bower; and in every place there was emptiness and desolation, and no single living creature beside themselves.

Greatly wondering, they left Narberth the next day and travelled the length and breadth of Dyved, seeking other folk; but all they found were forsaken homesteads and vanished flocks and people. Everywhere flourished rank weeds and wild beasts. For three years in Dyved they hunted the beasts for their food and ate roots and berries and the honey of wild bees, until the solitude oppressed their spirits and the lack of other human company weighed heavily on their hearts.

'We can no longer live in this manner,' said Manawyddan. 'Since we have lost wealth and warriors and all our possessions, let us go into England and follow some trade.'

To this all four agreed; and journeying into England, they came to the town of Hereford. There they found lodging and Manawyddan set up as a saddler. The saddles he made were good and strong, and he decorated them with blue enamel, so that they were finer than any other saddles made in Hereford; and soon there was no man in all the town who would buy a saddle from anyone but Manawyddan.

When the English saddlers saw how they were losing all their trade, they met together to discuss what they should do. 'Let us kill this stranger and his companions,' they decided.

But before they could do so, the four learnt of the plot and took counsel together as to how they should save themselves.

'Let us leave the town,' advised the peaceable Manawyddan.

'No,' said Pryderi. 'Let us rather defend ourselves against these saddlers and slay them all.'

'If we do that,' said Manawyddan, 'we shall be taken and cast into prison. That would be an ill fate. Let us instead go to another town and take up another trade.'

In the end it was his counsel that prevailed, and the four of them left

Hereford secretly and journeyed to the town of Ludlow; and there Manawyddan and Pryderi set up as makers of shields. The shields they made were firm and stout and cunningly decorated—in the manner of the saddles—with blue enamel. So speedily and so well they worked, that soon there was no warrior in all the town who would buy a shield of any other man. When the shieldmakers of Ludlow saw how their trade was lost, they met together in anger. 'Let us slay these two strangers,' they said.

But word came to the ears of Manawyddan and Pryderi of how the shieldmakers plotted against them.

'They will kill us all, Pryderi,' said Manawyddan.

'Before that happens,' said Pryderi, 'let us fall upon the knaves and kill them first.'

'No,' said Manawyddan. 'For if we succeeded, the usurper Caswallawn would hear of it and send his men against us. It would be better to go to another town and take up another trade.'

So the four left Ludlow secretly and went to the town of Gloucester.

'What trade shall we follow here?' asked Pryderi.

'Let us make shoes,' said Manawyddan. 'For cobblers are a poor-spirited lot, and maybe will not molest us.'

'I know nothing of shoemaking,' objected Pryderi.

'I will teach you,' said Manawyddan. He bought the finest dressed leather that was to be had in the town and he cut and shaped it and showed Pryderi how to stitch it; then he went to the best goldsmith in Gloucester and had him make gilded fastenings for the shoes; and while these clasps were being made, Manawyddan looked on carefully, until he had learnt the manner of making them. Then he and Pryderi made more shoes, and the gilded fastenings they made also; and so service-able and fine their shoes were, that soon there was no one in all Gloucester who would buy shoes or riding-boots from any man save Manawyddan and Pryderi.

Poor-spirited though Manawyddan might have thought them, when the cobblers of Gloucester saw their livelihood lost and themselves likely to starve, they met together and determined to kill the strangers.

But, as before, Manawyddan learnt of the plotting. 'The cobblers have a mind to kill us, Pryderi,' he said.

'Who are they to seek to kill us, these base-born wretches?' exclaimed Pryderi. 'Let us slay them first.'

'No,' said Manawyddan. 'Let us instead leave England—for we have had enough of England—and return to our own home in Dyved.'

So Manawyddan and Pryderi, Rhiannon and Kicva, journeyed back to Narberth, taking hounds with them, and there in the deserted castle they kindled fire again on the cold hearthstone; and each day Manawyddan and Pryderi went out with the hounds and hunted and fished, and the game they brought home to the empty, echoing halls was cooked by Rhiannon and Kicva. And thus the four of them lived, month after month.

After a year had passed in this manner, one morning when Manawyddan and Pryderi went out to hunt, a short way from Narberth their hounds ran questing into a thicket and after a moment ran out again, growling, with their backs bristling, and obviously afraid.

'Let us see what is hidden in that thicket, to make the hounds so fearful,' said Pryderi, and they went towards the trees. As they approached, a huge boar, white as snow and gleaming, rose up from the undergrowth. Urged on by their masters, the hounds grew bolder and returned to the attack, and the white boar ran a short distance with the hounds after him, before turning at bay. Manawyddan and Pryderi ran after the hounds, and as soon as they had come up to them, the boar ran on again for a little way, before turning once more to face the hounds until the men caught up with them. And so it went in this fashion, with the boar leading Manawyddan and Pryderi ever a little farther onwards until they came before a tall castle, in a place where they had never before seen any dwelling. Then, in a flash, the white boar was away from them and into the castle, with the hounds after him.

Manawyddan and Pryderi stood before the castle, marvelling at it, but neither hounds nor white boar came out again.

'I am going in to fetch out the hounds,' said Pryderi after a while.

'This castle is yet another enchantment, like that which is on all the land of Dyved already,' warned Manawyddan. 'We would be wise to take care.'

'The hounds were good and true. I cannot abandon them.' And Pryderi went into the castle.

Within the castle walls all was still and silent, with neither boar nor hounds anywhere, and no sign of any other creature. But in the middle of the courtyard there was a fountain with a wide curb of marble all about it; and above a marble slab beside the fountain, there was a golden bowl, hanging by four seemingly endless golden chains, suspended from the empty air.

Filled with admiration at the beauty of the bowl and its fine workmanship, Pryderi stepped upon the marble slab and laid hold of the bowl. Immediately his hands stuck fast to the bowl and his feet to the marble slab, and there he stood, unable to move or to utter a single word.

Outside the castle Manawyddan waited, full of foreboding. When evening came, and there had been neither sight nor sound of Pryderi or the hounds, he gave up hope and returned slowly and sadly to Narberth. As he entered the great hall, Rhiannon looked up at him. 'Where is my son, and where are the hounds?'

When Manawyddan had told her, she said bitterly, 'You have been a poor friend to one who was a good friend to you.'

'At least one of us has returned to care for you and Kicva,' said Manawyddan. 'Would you rather have lost us both?'

She paid no heed to him, but taking up her mantle, flung it about her and hurried off in the dusk towards the spot on which he had told her the strange castle had appeared. With no thought of the danger, she went through the tall gates and on into the courtyard, and there she saw Pryderi, standing by the fountain, his hands on the golden bowl. She ran towards him. 'My son, what are you doing here? Let this bowl be, and come home.' She laid her hands upon the bowl to take it from him, but immediately her hands stuck fast to its rim, and her feet stuck fast to the marble slab, and she, like Pryderi, was a prisoner. Then there was a great roll of thunder and a thick mist fell all about them; and when it had cleared away, all was gone: Pryderi, Rhiannon, hounds and boar, the fountain, the bowl and the whole castle.

In the morning, surveying the spot where the castle had stood, Kicva wept. 'My husband is gone. I care not whether I live or die.'

'Take courage, Kicva,' said Manawyddan, for all his own sorrow. 'You have yet me to protect you, and no woman ever had a truer friend than I shall be to you.'

Kicva dried her tears. 'That is so, lord. Yet what is best for us to do?'

'We have lost our hounds. It is a poor way to live, hunting without hounds, as we learnt before. Let us go again into England.'

'How shall we live there?' she asked.

'Why, as we did when there were four of us: by following a trade.'

'What trade will you follow? This time, I beg you, lord, let it be a fitting one.'

'I was a good cobbler, Kicva. I shall make shoes again.'

'That is hardly a fitting trade for one such as you,' she answered. But she went with him to the town of Gloucester, and there, as formerly, he made shoes and riding-boots so fine and serviceable that soon no man would buy any but his; and, as before, the other cobblers plotted against his life.

Kicva learnt of this and said to him, 'Must you bear such treatment from base-born cobblers?'

'No,' he replied. 'Let us go home to Dyved.'

So they set off for Narberth, Manawyddan carrying with him a sack of corn; and they were glad when they reached home again, for all that there were but the two of them left. Manawyddan hunted and trapped and fished, and Kicva searched for roots and herbs and cooked; and when the spring came, Manawyddan dug and tilled three fields and sowed them with the corn that he had carried on his back from England. The days passed and the corn sprouted sharp and green, the rain fell and it grew straight and tall, the sun shone and it turned heavy and golden; and so the year came to harvest-time.

One evening Manawyddan looked at his first field and saw that the corn was ready to cut. 'Tomorrow I shall reap this field,' he thought.

At dawn he returned to the field with a sickle and found nothing there but bare straw standing—every ear of corn had been cut from its stalk so that there was not a single ear remaining. Greatly troubled, he went to his second field and saw that there, also, the corn was ripe. 'Tomorrow I shall reap this field,' he thought. But when he came at dawn, he found once again only the straw standing stiff and bare, and not a single ear of corn. 'Alas!' he cried. 'Our unknown enemy is determined to destroy us utterly. After all these years, is his spite against the land of Dyved not appeased?' He went on to the third field and saw how that, too, stood ripe and ready for the sickle. 'This is the last field,' he thought. 'Tonight I shall watch beside it, and if the strength of one warrior can save the crop, then it shall be saved.'

When dusk came he took leave of Kicva, and carrying his weapons, went out to the field and stood guard over his crop. At midnight he heard a great squeaking all about him and a rustling amongst the corn stalks, and then he was aware of a huge army of mice—countless numbers of them—and each mouse running up a corn stalk until it bent beneath its weight, cutting through the stalk with sharp little teeth, then dropping to the ground and so away, carrying the ear of corn. And in all the field, there was no single stalk without a mouse.

In great anger Manawyddan rushed upon the mice, striking right and left at them—but always missing, they were so small and quick. And into the darkness vanished the huge army of mice and all the ears of corn. Manawyddan looked about him, furious and despairing, and espied one mouse, heavier and slower than the others, which had lagged behind them, dragging its ear of corn. He pounced and caught the mouse, dropped it into his glove and fastened the mouth of the glove with a cord. Weary and wrathful, he returned to Kicva.

She sat up on her bed and watched him as he stirred the fire and hung up the glove from a peg. 'What have you there, lord?'

'A thief whom I caught robbing me.'

'What sort of a thief is it that one can put into a glove?'

He told her of the army of mice and of the one which he had caught because it was less nimble than the rest. 'Tomorrow I will hang it,' he said grimly. 'And if I had them all, I swear they all should hang.'

'It is indeed a strange thing that you have told me tonight,' said Kicva. 'But, lord, is it fitting that one so great as you should so much demean himself as to hang a petty creature like a mouse?'

'If I had them all, I would hang them all,' he repeated. 'But since I have only this one, it shall hang for the rest.'

Kicva shrugged her shoulders. 'There is no reason why I should wish to spare the mouse, save for the sake of your dignity. Do as you will with it.' And she lay down again to sleep.

In the morning Manawyddan climbed to the top of the green hill which stood beside the castle of Narberth, taking the mouse with him. There at the very top of the hill he set up two forked twigs. At that moment he looked up and saw approaching the hill, on an old nag, a poor clerk, clad in worn and threadbare garments, and he was amazed at the sight, for he had seen no one in all Dyved for seven years, save only Pryderi, Rhiannon, Kicva and himself.

The clerk called out to him, 'Greetings to you, lord.'

'Greetings to you, stranger,' replied Manawyddan. 'From where do you come?'

'From England, lord, where I have been singing my songs. But if you will forgive my curiosity, lord, what are you doing?'

'I am hanging a thief whom I caught robbing me.'

'But is that not a mouse which I see in your hands, lord?'

'It is.'

'Lord, it is ill to see a man of your nobility and rank hanging such miserable vermin as a mouse. Let it go free, lord.'

'I caught it robbing me,' said Manawyddan, 'and by my word, I shall not let it go free.'

The clerk fumbled in his threadbare garments. 'Lord, I have here a silver piece which was given to me as alms in England. I will give it to you if you will let the mouse go free.'

'I will neither free it nor sell it.' Manawyddan turned away, and the clerk rode out of sight.

Manawyddan was just laying a cross-beam on the two forks when he looked up and saw a neatly clad priest approaching him, riding on a sturdy horse with handsome trappings. 'Greetings to you, lord,' the priest called out.

'Greetings to you, priest,' replied Manawyddan, marvelling that after seven years he should see two strangers within a minute of each other.

'May I ask, lord, what you are doing?'

'I am hanging a thief whom I caught robbing me.'

'What manner of thief, lord?'

'A thief in the form of a mouse, priest. I caught it robbing me, and it shall suffer the fate of a thief.'

'Lord,' said the priest, 'rather than see you lay hands on such a paltry creature as a mouse, I will buy it from you.'

'I have declared that I will neither free it nor sell it,' said Manawyddan.

'It is indeed true, lord, that a mouse is worthless and has no price, but for the sake of your dignity I will give you three silver pieces to let it go free.'

'I will take no price for this mouse,' exclaimed Manawyddan. 'I have said I will hang it, and hang it I shall.' And he turned away from the priest, who rode on out of sight.

Manawyddan made a slip-knot in a piece of cord and put it about the neck of the mouse; then he heard a jingling of harness and a tramping of hooves and he looked up to see a richly clad bishop approaching with his retinue: pack-horses and serving-men and a great train of followers. The bishop dismounted from his horse and made haste up the hillside towards Manawyddan.

Manawyddan stood and watched him come. 'Greetings, bishop,' he said.

'Greetings and blessings upon you, lord,' said the bishop. 'What are you doing?'

'Hanging a thief whom I caught robbing me.'

'Is that not a mouse which I see in your hand?'

'It is a mouse, and it was robbing me.'

'Was it, indeed?' said the bishop. 'Then since I have come by at this time, let me do the creature a kindness and ransom it. I will give you seven silver pieces to let her go free.'

'No,' said Manawyddan.

'I will give you four and twenty silver pieces,' said the bishop.

'For twice as much I would not let this thief go free.'

The bishop flung out his hand towards his retinue. 'I will give you as well all the horses of my followers and the seven pack-horses and their seven loads of baggage.'

Manawyddan looked thoughtfully at the bishop through narrowed eyes. 'I will not take them,' he said. Then he looked down at the mouse in his hands and tightened the noose about its neck.

'Name your own price,' said the bishop quickly.

Manawyddan looked up. 'Release Pryderi and Rhiannon.'

'Willingly.' The bishop held out his hand. 'Now let the mouse go free.'

'Not yet. There is more I want. Take the spell from the land of Dyved.'

'It shall be done. Now let her go.'

'Not yet.' Manawyddan looked at the mouse. 'First tell me who she is.'

'She is my wife. I beg of you, let her go free.'

'Not before you have told me your name and why you have come to Dyved. For you are no bishop, nor yet a priest or a clerk.'

'I am Llwyd, son of Kilcoed, and it was I who cast the spell upon Dyved for the sake of my friendship with Gwawl, who was suitor to Rhiannon and shamefully tricked and treated by her and by Pwyll. Upon Pwyll, Gwawl was never avenged, but through me he has been avenged upon Rhiannon and upon Pwyll's son, and upon all the land of Dyved. It was my men whom I changed into mice, that they might destroy your corn. On two nights my men went alone to your fields, but on the third night my wife and her women came to me and asked that they, also, might take part in the vengeance. This I granted and changed them, too, into mice. But my wife is with child, and she was slow to run from you, and so you caught her and hold her in your hand. Now, Manawyddan, son of Llyr, I have told you all you asked: give her back to me.'

'Not until you have sworn never again to put an enchantment upon the land of Dyved.'

'I swear it. Now give me my wife.'

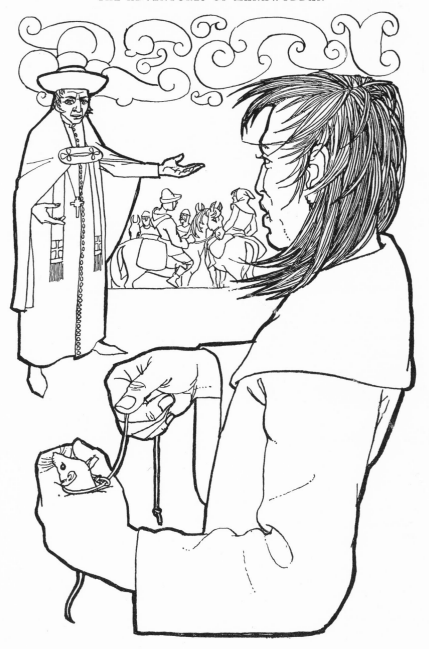

'Not yet.'

'What more can you ask of me?' exclaimed Llwyd.

'First swear that you will take no vengeance for this day on Pryderi or on Rhiannon or on me.'

'I swear it,' said Llwyd. 'And wisely did you ask that, for my vengeance was prepared for you already.'

Manawyddan smiled. 'I guessed so.'

'Now, Manawyddan, give me my wife.'

'Not until I see Pryderi and Rhiannon before me,' said Manawyddan.

'See, here they come,' said Llwyd.

Manawyddan looked; and indeed, there were Pryderi and Rhiannon, climbing the hill towards him. He hastened to them and embraced them eagerly, and there was great joy between them.

'Son of Llyr,' said Llwyd, 'I have done all you demanded. Give me back my wife.'

Smiling, Manawyddan replied to him, 'Gladly.' He opened his hand and stooped down and laid the mouse upon the grass. Llwyd stepped forward and touched her with his staff and instantly she was transformed into a fair young woman. He put his arm about her. 'Look around you,' he said to the others, 'and see how the enchantment is lifted from the land of Dyved.'

They did so, and they saw how once again there were cattle and flocks grazing, and fields of corn and barley, and all about the walls of Narberth were clustered the dwellings of the peasants; and in all things the land of Dyved was as it had been before, in its best and most prosperous days.

Llwyd went with his wife and his followers back to his own country; and Manawyddan and Pryderi and Rhiannon walked joyfully into Narberth to where Kicva waited; and the four of them dwelt happily together among their own folk for many years.

★　★　★

Pryderi, like his father Pwyll, was originally a god of the underworld. Gwawl, whose name still means 'light' in Welsh, was a solar deity who had been worsted by Pwyll at the time of his marriage to Rhiannon, whose suitors they both had been.

With regard to the hanging of the mouse: old Welsh law decreed that a thief should be hanged if he were caught in possession of the stolen goods. But where he was taken without the goods, he could be redeemed at a price which varied with the value of the stolen property. The mouse in the story had, in fact, been caught in possession of the stolen goods; but Welsh law held that, since no owner could, without any doubt, identify his own corn, a theft of corn should always be treated as one where the thief had not been taken with the goods in his possession, and could therefore be redeemed.

3

MIDIR AND ETAIN

This next Irish story takes place after the people of Dana have removed themselves from the regions frequented by the invading men and now dwell in their own enchanted homes beneath the sea, on faraway islands, or in the interior of the green hills of Ireland. But they still leave their homes when it pleases them, and they still have contact with mortals, either because they favour them or because they wish for their help.

It is from the hills in which so many of them were thought to live, that the name was derived by which the gods of Ireland came to be collectively known: the Aes Sidhe. Sidh (plural sidhe) is the Gaelic for a mound or small hill; hence these dwellers in the hills were known as the Aes Sidhe—the People of the Hills—or, more shortly, the Sidhe, the name by which the fairies into whom the ancient gods were eventually debased are known in Ireland today.

Midir's song, in which he tells Etain of the delights of his land, is typical of many such descriptions of the homes of the immortals to be found in early Irish writings. In my version here, I have tried not to wander too far from a literal translation of the Gaelic, because I felt that it would be a pity to lose the simplicity of those pleasures which appealed to the ancient poet, and his rather charming and unexpected metaphors.

* * *

Midir the Proud, the god of the underworld, had two wives, Fuamnach and the lovely Etain of the Horses. Etain is said to have been so beautiful that hers was the standard for all beauty in later years, when it was reckoned the highest praise a woman could have, that it should be said of her: 'She is as fair as Etain.'

Because Midir loved Etain the better, Fuamnach was jealous of her; and by her arts, unknown to Midir, she changed her into a butterfly, and then, raising a great tempest, blew her far from Midir's home. For seven long years the butterfly was tossed through the sky by the winds, until she was at last blown into the palace of Angus of the Birds, the god of love. Since one immortal can always recognize another, no matter in what shape either may be, Angus knew Etain immediately, and kept her with him in his palace by the River Boyne. Angus—about whose head ever fluttered little birds which were said to be his kisses—could not break the whole of the enchantment that Fuamnach had put on Etain, but half of it he broke, so that though she had to remain a butterfly while daylight lasted, during the hours of night she had once again her own fair shape. Angus built her a bower of glass, filled with sweet-scented, growing herbs and flowers, and this bower he carried with him wherever he went, covered with a veil of purple, that Etain might be invisible to all eyes but his. And though Midir searched everywhere for his lost wife, he could not find her.

It chanced, however, that Fuamnach learnt that Etain was in the care of Angus, and happy with him, and her hatred for her rival would not let her rest until she had put an end to Etain's happiness. She said to Midir, who had an old quarrel with Angus of the Birds, 'It is time that you were reconciled with your brother Angus. Invite him to your palace for a feasting and I will make peace between the two of you.'

Midir did as she counselled; and, since he could not bring Etain in her glass bower with him into Midir's home, when Angus went to his brother, he left her alone in his palace by the Boyne. There Fuamnach went, and raising up another tempest, she blew Etain, still in the shape of a butterfly, out of the bower and away across Ireland.

When Angus reached Midir's palace and found that Fuamnach was not there with Midir to receive him, he guessed that she meant mischief to Etain, so he confessed to his brother that he had Etain in his own palace; and Midir bade him go at once and see that she was safe. But when Angus came to the Boyne, he found Etain gone and the glass bower empty. So he followed the tracks of Fuamnach until he caught up with her, then he destroyed her and cut off her head; and thus ended Midir's jealous wife.

As for Etain, once again for seven years she was blown by the winds about the sky; until one day she was blown down the smoke-hole of the house of a chieftain named Etar, and she fell into the drinking-cup of Etar's wife, just as she was about to drink from it; and Etar's wife swallowed the butterfly. But the immortals do not perish so easily, and

in due course of time, Etain was born as Etar's daughter, with all her own beauty—so that she grew into the fairest woman ever seen in Ireland—yet with no memory of who she had been before her birth to Etar's wife, and no thought that she was other than a mortal maiden.

Now, at that time the High King of Ireland was Eochai. He was a young man and but newly crowned, and he had no queen. Before he had been king a year, as was the custom, he summoned all his lords and chieftains to his court at Tara for an assembly; but they all made one reply to his summons, 'We will not come to Tara until you take a wife; for it is unfitting that any lord should be without a wife, and any king without a queen.'

So Eochai sent out his men into every part of Ireland, bidding them seek a wife for him, a maiden who was both beautiful and of high birth. And in Ulster, in the house of Etar the chieftain, they found Etain and carried word of her back to Tara to the High King.

Eochai himself drove into Ulster to see her, and the first sight he had of her was at the spring outside her father's house, where she had gone to wash her hair. She was wearing a purple cloak and a mantle with silver fringes over a gown of green silk with red and gold embroidery. Her yellow hair was braided into eight long strands, each tipped with a little golden ball; and at the moment that Eochai saw her from his chariot, she was unplaiting her hair to wash it in a silver basin set with red stones.

The king reined in his horses, amazed at her beauty, and suddenly she was aware of him and looked up, so that he saw that her eyes were the colour of bluebells and he knew at once that here, indeed, was the wife he wanted.

Her father Etar, and Etain herself, were willing; and when Eochai had paid the bride-price for her, he married her and took her back with him to Tara; and there they were happy together.

But Midir the Proud was still searching for his lost Etain, and at last in Tara he found her; and there he contrived to meet her, unseen of any save her.

'Who are you,' she asked, 'and why do you come to me?'

'It is fitting that I should come to you,' replied Midir, 'for when you were Etain of the Horses, I was your husband.'

'I never had a husband before King Eochai. What name do you call yourself, stranger?'

'I am Midir, son of the Dagda.'

But she did not believe him, because she remembered nothing before her birth to Etar's wife. 'If it truly was as you say,' she challenged him, 'why am I not still your wife?'

'We were parted by the jealousy and the spells of Fuamnach, your rival. But now that I have found you again, my Etain, come back with me to our own land and our people.' And he sang to her of the joys of his enchanted land and of the people of Dana.

> O gold-haired one, will you come with me
> Into a land of enchanted music?
> There, all are beautiful, all are fair,
> With snow-white skin and primrose hair.

In that land all share alike.
White show their teeth, black their arched brows;
Each cheek glows with the foxglove's red,
And eyes are bright in each proud head.

The warmth of the heather reflects on each neck,
And eyes are the hue of a blackbird's egg.
Though the wide plains of Ireland are pleasant to see,
They are but a desert to the plains of the Sidhe.

Though you think the ale strong which in Ireland you
                                                    drink,
The ale in that land is far stronger.
Never youth before age does discourteously stand,
For old there are none in that marvellous land.

The streams of that land flow smooth and clear;
And mead and wine flow as freely as water.
There, all are free from blemish and sin,
Their bodies as pure as the minds within.

Nothing to us is invisible;
There is nowhere we cannot go;
Yet no one sees us as we pass by,
Veiled by a mist from each mortal eye.

There shall be, if you come to my land,
A golden crown for your head;
There, your mirth and your feasting shall never be done.
Come with me now, O fair-haired one.

He held out his hands to her and smiled; but she did not smile back.
'I know neither your kindred nor your lineage, and nothing of yourself save what you have told me—and that may well be lies. Would you
have me give up the High King of Ireland to go with you?' She stared
at him, her head held high. 'I will go with you to your country when
King Eochai gives me to you; not before.' And certain that such a
thing would never come to pass, she turned and left him.

One summer's morning, a little time after this, King Eochai rose very early and went and stood upon the ramparts of Tara looking out across the plain that stretched before him, when suddenly he was aware of a young warrior standing at his side. The young man wore a purple tunic and carried a jewelled shield and a spear. His golden hair was long and as bright as the iris that grows in the streams, and his grey eyes shone. Eochai wondered to see him there, for he knew that the stranger had not been in the hall the evening before, and it was as yet too early in the morning for the gates of Tara to have been opened. Nevertheless he held his peace and said no word of this.

'My greetings to you, young warrior. You are welcome.'

Midir smiled. 'You have received me as I knew you would, King Eochai.'

'You are a stranger to us in Tara,' said the king.

'But you are no stranger to me, King Eochai.'

'Who are you?'

'I am Midir, son of the Dagda.'

'Why have you come here?'

'To play chess with you.'

Now, Eochai was a renowned chess player, and he never feared the outcome of a game. He laughed. 'You have chosen a skilled opponent.'

'I am no mean player myself,' said Midir, 'so let us test your skill.'

'Willingly,' said Eochai. 'But the chessboard is in the queen's apartments, and she is still sleeping.'

'I have with me a chessboard which I do not doubt is the equal of yours.' Midir took from the folds of his cloak a jewelled, silver chessboard and a bag of golden chessmen. He set out the pieces on the board and they sat down to play.

Eochai, very sure of his skill, said, 'I never play without a stake.'

'Name your stake,' said Midir.

'Let the loser do whatever the victor may demand of him,' said Eochai.

To this Midir agreed; and they played their first game and Midir lost.

'It is my demand that you shall clear away all rocks and stones from the plains of Meath,' said Eochai.

'It shall be done,' said Midir.

They played again; and again Eochai won.

41

'It is my demand that you shall remove the coarse rushes which grow all about the stronghold of Teffa, and make the land fertile.'

'It shall be done.'

They played again; and yet once more Eochai won.

'It is my demand that you shall cut down the Forest of Breg.'

'It shall be done.'

One more time they played; and Eochai won.

'It is my demand that you shall build for me a road across the Bog of Lamrach.'

'It shall be done.'

At sunset Midir went to perform the tasks. 'They will be finished before morning,' he said. 'Yet let no man watch the work being done.'

He called up the people of Dana, and all night they laboured; and by dawn all rocks and stones were cleared from the plains of Meath, there were no rushes or rank growth left around the stronghold of Teffa, the Forest of Breg had been cut down, and there was a road across the Bog of Lamrach—yet this road was unfinished; the reason for this being that Eochai sent his steward to spy on the people of Dana as they worked, and he saw them labouring at the building of the road and singing as they toiled. He saw, also, that they harnessed their oxen for the dragging of stones for the road, with yokes about their necks, instead of with leather bands about their foreheads, as did the men of Ireland. The steward thought that this was a far better way than theirs, and he hastened home at dawn to tell Eochai. But because the people of Dana had been observed as they laboured, there was for ever after a breach in the road across the bog which could never be mended by any man.

When Eochai heard how the people of Dana yoked their oxen about the shoulders, he ordered that all the men in Ireland were to do like-wise when they ploughed; and for that he was ever after known as Eochai Airem—Eochai the Ploughman.

But that morning, after the tasks had been completed, while Eochai and his steward were still speaking together of the yoking of the oxen, Midir came again to Tara, and this time he was frowning and angry. Eochai and his steward looked up to see him before them, and Eochai rose to welcome him; but Midir said, 'Your demands were excessive, and the tasks you put upon me better fitted for a slave; and you sent a

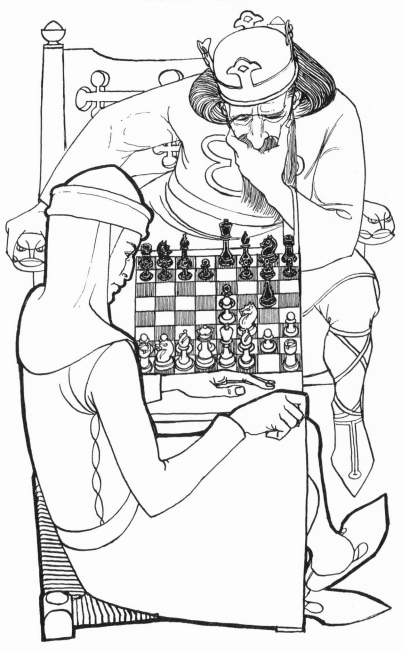

man to watch my people, though I had forbidden it. Yet all that you demanded I have done, and done well, but now I am angered against you, King Eochai.'

'You agreed to the stake for each game,' said Eochai. 'But I am a peaceable man and I return not anger for anger. Tell me, what satisfaction can I offer you?'

'Let us play one last game of chess.'

'Willingly,' said Eochai. 'For what stake shall we play this time?'

'The same stake as before. That the victor shall demand what he will of the loser.'

'I agree to that,' said Eochai.

They played; and this time Eochai lost.

'It is you have won this last game,' he said to Midir, surprised.

'Had I wished it so, I could have won the first game, and all the others, also,' said Midir.

'What do you demand of me?' asked Eochai.

'That I may hold the queen in my arms and kiss her once.'

When Eochai heard this, he was silent for a long time, for he was afraid. Then he said, 'If you come to Tara a month from this day, you shall have what you demand.'

To this Midir agreed, and he went from the High King's house.

Eochai immediately sent word to all his chieftains, lords and warriors, that they should come with their men to Tara, ready for battle; and by the time a month had passed, Tara was guarded by a huge army. The stronghold was encircled by ring upon ring of armed men, whose sharp spears were as many as the blades of grass upon the plain that stretched before the walls of Tara; while the High King's house itself was locked and barred against all comers; for Eochai thought that Midir would arrive with a great host of the people of Dana to claim Etain.

But on the evening of the appointed day, as Eochai and his lords were sitting down to meat and Etain and her maidens were pouring their drink for them, Midir suddenly appeared in the hall before them, alone. This time the glory of his immortality was all about him, and everyone in the hall fell silent in awe, and only Eochai rose to greet him. But Etain, gazing at him, fairer and more splendid than any mortal man, began, as through a mist, to remember.

'You are welcome to Tara,' said Eochai, his heart cold and heavy.

Midir smiled a little. 'You have received me as I expected you to receive me, King Eochai. Now pay me your debt, for I paid all you demanded of me.'

'Give me longer to consider the matter,' said Eochai desperately.

'Come,' said Midir, 'give me Etain, for you promised her to me.'

When she heard this, Etain blushed and hung her head in shame, that the king should have so lightly given her to another. But Midir said to her gently, 'Do not blush, for there is no shame to you in this thing. For a long time I sought you throughout Ireland, and I have not taken you until Eochai permitted it. The time has now come for you to return to your own land. You yourself said that you would come with me if your husband gave you to me.'

'That is true,' said Etain in a low voice. 'Take me, if he has indeed given me to you.'

'I have not given you to him,' cried Eochai. He turned to Midir. 'You demanded of me only that you should hold Etain in your arms and kiss her once. Do it now, in this hall, before the eyes of all of us here, that I may be quit of my debt.'

'It shall be done,' said Midir. He took his spear in his left hand and put his right arm about Etain and kissed her; and in that instant she remembered everything that had happened before she was born to Etar's wife; and she was no longer Etain, daughter of Etar, wife of the High King Eochai—she was Etain of the Horses, Etain the immortal, the beloved wife of Midir the Proud. Then Midir and Etain rose up into the air and passed through a roof-window in the hall and out of sight.

There was great confusion and shouting and anger, and Eochai and his guests ran out from the hall. But all they could see were two white swans in the air, circling high above Tara in the last rays of the setting sun.

4

THE BRIDE-PRICE FOR OLWEN

In this story, King Arthur is neither the ancient British chieftain of history and the Celtic deity with whom the historical Arthur became confused in folk-memory, nor the pattern of chivalry familiar to us from the pages of Malory. He is somewhere in between the two conceptions: a fine warrior and the centre of a gathering of other brilliant warriors—yet for all that, not quite an earthly king. But if there is something strange about Arthur, several of his followers are even stranger. In the court of this Arthur his companions Kei and Bedwyr—Malory's Sir Kay the Seneschal and Sir Bedivere—rub shoulders with the one-time gods of Britain: Manawyddan, son of Llyr, Gwyn of the underworld and his natural rival, Gwythyr, a sky-god, and others.

In this story, too, forming the bride-price for Olwen, we meet the Thirteen Treasures of Britain which were famed in ancient legend; and we are treated to a succession of adventures—some mediaeval and some of great antiquity— several of which are told in detail, while others are sketched very briefly. The tale as we have it is not complete: our appetite is whetted by the mention of a number of adventures which are then never related. The story of the winning of Olwen by Kilhwch was no doubt of the type which could be lengthened or shortened by the addition or exclusion of certain incidents, according to the time at the disposal of the teller. Also, in a fluid framework such as is provided by this story, the teller could suit the interests of his listeners and make reference to heroes and adventures connected with the locality in which he found himself on the occasion of the recital.

★　★　★

There was once a king in Wales named Kilydd who had a fair young queen. A son was born to them whom they named Kilhwch; and at his birth, as was the custom, he was sent from his father's castle and given into the charge of a foster-mother. Soon after, the queen fell ill, and knowing that her end was near, she sent for her husband. 'Lord,' she said to him, 'I shall die of this sickness and it will come to your mind to take another wife. I cannot bear the thought that our son should have a stepmother who might not love him, so I charge you not to marry again until you shall see a briar with two heads growing on my grave.' And this the king promised her.

Unknown to the king, she then sent for her old teacher and instructor and bade him keep her grave always clear of all weeds and plants, so that no briar might ever flourish upon it. After that she died.

For seven years the old teacher did as the queen had bidden him, and though the king sent a man each day to the grave to see if a briar might yet be growing on it, there was never the smallest weed or blade of grass to be seen. But at last the teacher grew too old and became neglectful, and by the end of the seventh year he was no longer going to the grave. Then, one morning as the king rode out hunting, he passed by the queen's grave and he saw that upon it there was growing a briar with two heads. 'It is time for me to take another wife,' he said.

He asked his counsellors where he should look for a queen, and after thought, one of them replied, 'There is no woman worthy of you, lord, save only the wife of King Doged.'

So Kilydd made war on King Doged, defeated him and slew him, winning his lands for himself; and his wife, together with her young daughter, he carried off to his own castle, and he married her. But he did not tell her that he had a son by his first queen; and Kilhwch himself he left in the care of foster-parents.

Time passed, and one day the new queen was out walking near the castle when she came to the hut of an old witch and went inside. 'Tell me, old woman,' she said, 'since no one else has seen fit to do so, where are the children of the man who won me by the sword and carried me off by force?'

The toothless old witch looked at the queen and said, 'He has no children, lady.'

'Wretched indeed I am,' exclaimed the queen bitterly, 'to have been widowed and wedded by a childless man.'

The old witch was moved to pity and she came closer and whispered, 'Do not grieve, lady, for it is my belief that you, and no other, will give the king an heir. And besides, though you have not been told it, he has a son.'

Rejoicing, the queen returned home and went to the king demanding, 'Why have you hidden your son from me?'

'Lady,' said the king, 'I shall do so no longer.' He sent for Kilhwch, and the boy came to court.

When the queen saw how handsome and tall her stepson was, she was glad and said to him, 'You seem to me to be of an age to take a wife. I have a daughter, of equal years with you, fair enough for any prince. I would have you marry my daughter.'

'Lady,' said Kilhwch, 'I am too young to take a wife. Do not ask me to marry your daughter.'

The queen instantly grew angry, thinking her daughter slighted. 'You have refused my daughter, therefore I lay this fate on you: you shall have no wife save Olwen, daughter of Hawthorn the Chief Giant. Either you marry Olwen, or you die unwed.'

Though he had never seen, or even heard of Olwen, at the mention of her name the boy changed colour, thinking how fine a wife she sounded for any youth: Olwen, daughter of the Chief Giant.

His father noticed and called to him, 'What ails you, my son, that you blush and say nothing?'

'Father,' replied Kilhwch, 'my stepmother has laid it on me to marry Olwen, daughter of Hawthorn the Chief Giant, or no one. I would go and find her this very moment, if I knew where she was to be found.'

'It should not be hard for you to find her, my son. You are cousin to King Arthur. Go to him, ask him to trim your hair for you, tell him what you have told me, and demand it of him as a boon that he and his men shall help you to find Olwen.'

Happily young Kilhwch set off for King Arthur's court with his father's blessing, riding upon a four-year-old horse with a dappled head whose trappings and saddle were gilded. He wore a mantle of purple trimmed with four golden apples, each one worth a hundred head of cattle. He held two sharp silver spears, a gold-hilted sword was slung about him, and he carried an ivory war-horn. Lightly his horse galloped, throwing up the turfs behind him like four swallows; and his two white and brindled greyhounds, with their golden collars set with rubies, ran bounding before the horse, now upon one side of him and now upon the other. And so Kilhwch came to Arthur's court one evening and called to the porter to let him in.

'I will not let you in,' said the porter.

'And why not?'

'Because the knife is in the meat, the drink is in the horn, there is merriment in the king's hall and Arthur has sat down to sup. No one may enter now, save only the son of a king or a craftsman bringing his craft. You will find food and a welcome in the guest hall, stranger.'

'I will sup with King Arthur or not at all,' said Kilhwch. 'Open the gate and let me in, or I will bring disgrace upon all the court. I will send up three shouts at the king's gate which shall be heard in Cornwall, in the north, and across the sea in Ireland.'

The porter shrugged his shoulders. 'You may shout all you please, stranger, but you shall not enter until I have spoken with the king.' And leaving Kilhwch at the gate, he went in to tell Arthur of the impetuous youth who waited outside. 'Never, lord,' said he to Arthur, 'have I seen so noble a youth.'

'If he is indeed such as you say,' said Arthur, 'then it is unfitting for him to be kept waiting outside in the wind and the rain. You entered here walking, let it be running that you go forth from this hall to welcome him in.'

The porter ran to throw open the gate, and Kilhwch rode through upon his horse, and on, right into the hall. 'Greetings, my lord king, to you and to all gathered here,' he said.

'And greetings to you, stranger,' replied Arthur. 'Sit down and eat and drink with us.'

'Lord,' said Kilhwch, 'I did not come here to eat and drink, but to ask a boon of you.'

Arthur, looking admiringly at him, smiled and said, 'You shall have whatever boon you care to ask of me, save only my ship, my royal robe, my sword, my spear, my shield, my dagger or my wife. Ask what else you will.'

'For now, I ask only that you should trim my hair, lord.'

'I will do that for you,' said Arthur; and with a golden comb and silver-handled shears, he trimmed Kilhwch's yellow hair, and by so doing, according to the custom, took Kilhwch under his protection. 'And now,' said Arthur, 'tell me who you are, stranger, for my heart warms to you, and I think that you and I will prove to be kinsmen.'

'I am Kilhwch, son of King Kilydd.'

'Then we are indeed kinsmen,' exclaimed Arthur, 'for you are my cousin.' He embraced him. 'Now ask anything you will of me, and I shall grant it.'

'Help me to win Olwen, daughter of Hawthorn the Chief Giant, for myself, for it is my destiny to have no other wife. I ask this boon of you, lord, and of all your warriors.'

'I have never heard of the maiden Olwen,' said Arthur, 'but I will send messengers throughout all Britain to seek her for you.'

And so indeed he did; yet by the end of a year the messengers had returned without news of Olwen.

'You have heard, Kilhwch,' said Arthur, 'Olwen is not to be found.'

'All other men have been granted by Arthur the boons which they desired, save only I,' said Kilhwch. 'If I leave your court without Olwen, all men shall learn of your broken promise, lord.'

'Do you reproach the king?' the great warrior Kei, Arthur's friend and counsellor, asked angrily. 'You have no right to do so. Come with me and with those others of us whom Arthur chooses, and we will seek for Olwen until either we have found her or you confess that she does not live and breathe in any place in the world.'

To this Kilhwch agreed, and he set out on his quest with Kei; and with them Arthur sent Bedwyr the One-Handed, whom none could equal in swiftness, nor in the speed with which he shed the blood of an enemy. From no enterprise on which Kei went would Bedwyr hold back, although Kei could breath nine days and nine nights under the water, and could last nine days and nine nights without sleep, and could, when it pleased him, make himself as tall as the tallest tree in the forest. And so hot was Kei's nature, that even when the rain poured down, he remained dry; and when it was coldest, he was as a fire to his companions. With them, also, Arthur sent Kynddelig the Guide, who could lead his comrades as well in a strange land as he could in his own; Gwrhyr the Interpreter, because he knew all tongues, both of men and beasts; Menw the Sorcerer, who could make his companions invisible when danger threatened; and his own nephew Gwalchmei, who never returned home without achieving a quest.

These seven set out together and journeyed many miles, until one day they came to a wide plain on which stood a fair castle. Near the castle there grazed a fine flock of sheep, guarded by a huge shepherd clad in skins, with his sheepdog at his side. The sheepdog was a shaggy mastiff, larger than a full-grown horse, and its breath burnt up the grass and the bushes and trees in its path.

The companions saw them both with some misgiving. 'Gwrhyr,' said Kei, 'go and greet yonder shepherd, for you are our spokesman.'

'Kei,' replied Gwrhyr, 'when I came on this quest I pledged myself to go as far as you went, but no farther.'

'Then let us go together to speak to him,' said Kei.

'Have no fear,' said Menw the Sorcerer, 'for I shall cast a spell upon that dog so that it cannot see you.' And he did so.

Kei and Gwrhyr the Interpreter went up to the shepherd and greeted him, and he greeted them in reply, but with little goodwill.

'Whose are these fine sheep, my friend?' they asked.

'Dull-witted indeed you are not to know that they are the sheep of Hawthorn the Chief Giant, whose castle stands yonder.'

The companions looked at each other rejoicing inwardly. 'And who are you, shepherd?' they all asked.

'I am Custennin, brother of the Chief Giant, and you see me as no more than his shepherd because my brother has despoiled me of all I possess. And now it is for you, strangers, to tell me who you are.'

'We come from King Arthur, and we seek Olwen, daughter of the Chief Giant, as a wife for Kilhwch here.'

'Alas for you then,' said Custennin, 'for no man has ever returned from that quest alive.'

They all went on to Custennin's house and his wife saw them coming and ran out to greet them, a tall, strong woman with mighty arms. She made to embrace Kei in welcome, but quickly he snatched up a log from a pile of firewood lying beside the house door, and thrust that into her arms instead. And well it was that he did so, for the log splintered in her grip. 'Woman,' laughed Kei, 'had you squeezed me in that fashion, no one anywhere would ever have been able to welcome me again.'

They entered the house and food and drink were brought, and then Custennin's wife opened a large stone chest which stood near the hearth, and out of it stepped a yellow-haired youth. 'This is the last of my four and twenty sons,' she said. 'All his brothers has Hawthorn slain—and I have little hope that he will spare this one.'

'Let him put himself under my protection,' said Kei, 'and he will not be slain unless I am slain also.'

While they ate, the woman asked them, 'Why have you come here, strangers?' and they told her, as they had told her husband.

'Alas!' she exclaimed. 'Go now, and quickly, before anyone from the castle has seen you. No man has returned from that quest alive.'

'No,' they said. 'We shall not go until we have seen Olwen.'

'Does Olwen ever come here, to this house?' asked Kei.

'Every Saturday she comes here to wash her hair,' said the woman. 'And in the basin where she washes her hair, she leaves all the rings from her fingers, and she never returns to fetch them, nor does she send her servants for them.'

'Will she come here if you bid her?' asked Kei.

'She will indeed. Yet first give me your word that you mean her no harm.'

'We give you our word,' they all said; and she sent to Olwen, bidding her come to her uncle's house.

Soon Olwen came. She was wearing a gown of flame-coloured silk and about her neck a golden collar set with pearls and rubies. Her hair was more yellow than the blossom of the broom, her skin was fairer than sea-foam, and her hands were paler than white campion flowers. Her glance was as bright as a young hawk's, her breast was whiter than the breast of a swan, and her cheeks were redder than foxgloves. And wherever she trod, four white clovers sprang up, and for this she was called Olwen—White Footprints.

She came into her uncle's house and sat down beside Kilhwch; and as soon as he saw her, he knew her. 'Lady,' he said, 'it is you whom I have sought and loved for many long days. Come away with me now.'

She shook her head. 'I may not go with you, since I have promised my father that I will not wed without his consent. For it is foretold that his life will last only so long as I am unwed. But if you would have my counsel, go to my father and ask for my hand, and whatever he demands of you as a bride-price, give it to him, and perhaps you may win me. But remember, deny him nothing, or you will not escape with your life.'

'I will do as you bid me, lady,' promised Kilhwch; and Olwen rose and left him and returned to the castle.

The seven companions made their way to the castle after her; and at each of the nine gates of the castle they slew one of the nine porters without any outcry, and nine watchdogs, also, they slew in silence; and then they went on into the great hall, to find Hawthorn the Chief Giant. Very hideous he was, with eyelids which hung like curtains before his eyes, and a thick, rough beard.

'Greetings to you, Hawthorn, Chief Giant,' they called out.

He gave them a sour welcome. 'Who are you and what do you want?'

'We have come to ask the hand of Olwen for Kilhwch, son of Kilydd.'

'Hey there, you rogues of servants!' Hawthorn shouted. 'Prop open my eyes that I may see what manner of man wishes to be my son-in-law.'

His servants hurried forward with two forked branches with which they raised his hanging eyelids from his eyes, and the Chief Giant looked searchingly at the seven companions. 'Come here again to-morrow, and you shall have my answer,' he said at last.

As they turned to go, he took up one of the three poisoned spears which lay beside him and flung it at them. But Bedwyr caught it with his one hand and flung it back, and it pierced Hawthorn through the thigh, so that he cried out, 'What a cursed savage son-in-law! I shall always walk the worse for his discourtesy. Ah, this iron bites like a gadfly. My curses on the smith who forged it and the anvil at which it was made.'

They passed that night in the house of Custennin the shepherd, and early the next morning they went again to the castle. 'Chief Giant,' they said, 'give us your daughter, or it will go ill with you.'

'No,' he said. 'Her four great grandfathers and her four great grandmothers are still alive. I must take counsel with them first. Begone.'

They turned to go and he took up the second of the poisoned spears and flung it after them. But Menw the Sorcerer caught it and flung it back again and it struck Hawthorn full in the chest and passed right through his body. 'What a cursed savage son-in-law!' he shouted. 'This iron bites like a horse-leech. Now, whenever I go up a hill, I shall be out of breath, with a pain in my chest; and it will have done my digestion no good. My curses on the smith who made it and the fire where it was heated.'

They spent that night, also, in the house of Custennin, and early the next morning they came again to the castle. The moment they stood before him, Hawthorn the Chief Giant said, 'Take care you cast no weapons at me today, unless you wish to die. Hey there, rogues of servants! Prop open my eyes, that I may see my son-in-law.'

As soon as the servants had done so, the Chief Giant took up the third poisoned spear and cast it at the companions; but this time Kilhwch caught it and cast it swiftly back, so that it pierced Hawthorn in the eyeball and came out through the back of his head.

'What a cursed savage son-in-law!' he howled. 'As long as I live, my sight will be the worse for this. Whenever I walk against the wind my eyes will water. I shall have headaches and a giddiness with every new moon. This iron bites like a mad dog. My curses on the fire where it was forged. Begone!'

After another night in Custennin's house, they came again to the castle. 'Throw no more weapons at us, Chief Giant,' they warned, 'unless you wish for more wounds.'

'Give me your daughter, Chief Giant,' said Kilhwch.

'Where is the man who wants my daughter? Come here where I can see you.'

A stool was set before him, and Kilhwch sat down upon it. When the props had been placed beneath his eyes, Hawthorn frowned at him. 'So it is you who wants my daughter,' he said.

'It is I,' replied Kilhwch.

'So be it. When you have done as I shall ask and brought me the things I shall name, you shall have my daughter.'

'Speak on, Chief Giant.'

'There is a wooded hill yonder,' said Hawthorn. 'Uproot the trees and level the hill, plough it, sow it and reap the harvest all in one day, that I may make bread from the grain for my daughter's wedding.'

Kilhwch thought of his cousin Arthur and all the help he would have from him. 'It will be easy for me to do that, though you may not think it so,' he said.

'There is more, which you will not find so easy,' said Hawthorn. 'Yonder lies a tilled field. In that field I sowed eighteen bushels of flax, the year I first met with the mother of my daughter. In all those years the flax has not sprouted. Give me back the flax seed, every grain of it,

that I may plant it in new land to make a linen veil for my daughter to wear at her wedding.'

'It will be easy for me to do that, though you may not think it so,' said Kilhwch.

'There is more, which you will not find so easy. For the wedding feast I want the cup of Llwyr to drink from—and not lightly will he part with it. I want the never-empty vessel of Gwyddno of the Long Legs to supply our meat—and not lightly will he part with it. I want the drinking-horn of Gawlgawd of Midlothian to drink from, the cauldron of Diurnach the Irishman to boil meat in, and the harp of Teirtu, which plays of itself, to make music for me—and not lightly will any one of them part with his possessions. And, besides these things, I would have the birds of Rhiannon to sing for my entertainment.'

'It will be easy for me to get those things, though you may not think it so.'

55

'There is more. I would shave my beard for the wedding feast. For a razor I want the tusk of Whitetusk the Chief Boar—Cado of North Britain must take charge of it for me—and I want the blood of the Black Witch, daughter of the White Witch, with which to soften my beard for the shaving.'

'It will be easy for me to get these things, though you may not think it so.'

'Wait! There is yet more. I must comb and trim my hair before the wedding, and no comb is stout enough and no shears sharp enough for my hair, save the comb and the shears that lie between the two ears of the enchanted boar Trwyth, who was once a king before he became a boar. And you cannot hunt Trwyth without the hound Drudwyn, and you cannot hold Drudwyn without the leash of Cors of the Hundred Claws and the collar of Canhastyr of the Hundred Hands and the chain of Kilydd of the Hundred Holds. There is but one huntsman who can hunt with Drudwyn and he is Mabon, son of Modron, and no man knows where he is save his cousin Eidoel—and as for Eidoel, he is deep in a dungeon. And to carry Mabon you will need the horse Gwyn Baymane, the steed of Gweddu, swift as a wave. And to hunt with Mabon you will need Gwyn, son of Nudd, and the Chief Huntsman of Ireland and the two hounds Aned and Aethlem, who are as swift as the wind, and the two whelps of the hound bitch Rhymi, who can be held only by a leash made of the beard of Dillus the Bearded—and the hairs must be plucked from Dillus's beard while he yet lives, or they will have no strength. With them all must go Arthur and his men to hunt the boar Trwyth: and no one can compel Arthur to hunt against his will.'

If Kilhwch had been daunted by Hawthorn's demands, he was at least cheered by the last, for Arthur had given him his promise of help. 'It will be easy for me to do all those things, though you may not think it so,' he said as confidently as he might.

'When you have hunted and caught the boar Trwyth,' added Hawthorn, 'do not think that you will be rid of your troubles, for Trwyth can only be slain with the sword of Gwrnach the giant—and Gwrnach will never give his sword as a gift to any man.'

'Nevertheless, it will be easy for me, though you may not think it so. My kinsman Arthur will help me and I shall win your daughter and you shall lose your life.' Kilhwch rose, and he and his companions left the castle of Hawthorn the Chief Giant to start at once on their quest, taking with them Custennin's son.

All that day they journeyed and at evening they came before a huge castle, the largest in the world. As they were admiring this castle, out through the gates came a huge black man, as large as any three ordinary men.

'Whose is this castle?' they asked him.

'Great fools you must be, all of you, if you do not know that this is the castle of Gwrnach the giant,' answered the black man with scorn.

A quick glance passed amongst the companions: here was one of the treasures they sought, the sword of Gwrnach the giant. 'What welcome can a stranger expect at the castle?' they asked.

'No one may enter who does not bring with him his craft, and no guest ever left Gwrnach's castle alive, so you had best have a care for yourselves, strangers,' said the black man, and went on his way.

With no hesitation they went on to the gates and Gwrhyr the Interpreter called out, 'Ho there, porter! Open the gates to us.'

'Only to a craftsman bringing his craft do I open these gates,' said the porter.

'Then you may open to me,' said Kei swiftly, 'for I bring my craft with me. I am a fine burnisher of swords, the best in the world.'

When the porter told this to Gwrnach, the giant said, 'I have great need of a man to burnish my sword. Bring him to me.'

So Kei went alone into the castle and came before the giant who asked him, 'Is it true that you can burnish a sword?'

'I can indeed,' replied Kei.

The giant sent for his sword and Kei took a whetstone from under his arm and began to burnish it. When he had burnished one side of the sword, he held it out to the giant that he might see. 'Is that work to your liking?' he asked.

The giant could not believe his eyes. 'I would give much that the whole of the sword might look like this. But it seems strange to me that one so skilled as you should travel alone, without company.'

'I have a companion,' said Kei, 'and though he has no skill in my craft, my friend Bedwyr has a skill of his own. The head of his spear can leave its shaft, draw blood from the wind and return again to its shaft.'

'That is indeed a wondrous skill,' marvelled the giant, and he bade the porter fetch Bedwyr.

The others, left outside, watched Bedwyr go with concern and much speculation, and wished to follow him. Profiting by the interest aroused in the castle by the two supposed craftsmen, the young son of Custennin showed an unexpected ability and, unnoticed by any of the giant's men, he managed to herd his five companions into the castle, where they might be near, should Kei and Bedwyr need them. For this the others praised him, saying, 'You must indeed be the best of all men at winning entrance to the house of an enemy.' And ever after he was known as Goreu—Best.

In the great hall of the castle Kei finished burnishing the sword and showed it to the giant, who was well pleased with his work. 'Give me the scabbard,' said Kei, 'for I would guess it to have worn thin and to have let in the damp which had rusted your sword.' He came close to the giant and took the scabbard from him, then, making as though he were about to put the sword into its scabbard, he turned swiftly and struck off the giant's head, even as Gwrnach leant forward to watch him. At the sounds of dismay which came from the giant's friends and followers, Kilhwch and the others ran into the hall, and between them the eight companions took and spoilt the castle. Then they returned to the court of Arthur, bearing with them the first which they had won of those things needed for the bride-price of Olwen: the sword of Gwrnach the giant.

Back in Arthur's court, they discussed with him which of the treasures they should seek next. 'Would it not be best that we find the huntsman Mabon, son of Modron, who is to have charge of Drudwyn? Should we not seek out Mabon's cousin Eidoel, since he alone can find Mabon for us?'

'Eidoel is imprisoned deep in the castle of Glini,' said Arthur. 'Let us go and fetch him out.'

With many warriors Arthur marched to the castle of Glini; and seeing the army approaching, Glini went up on his castle walls and called down to Arthur, 'Why have you come here to my home? I have neither riches nor merriment here, and my wheat and my oats are spent. What have I that you covet?'

'Only the prisoner from your dungeon, Glini,' said Arthur. 'Give me Eidoel and I will go and leave you in peace.'

So Eidoel was released and joyfully he came up to the light of the day, and went with Arthur from the castle of Glini.

'Eidoel,' asked Arthur, 'where may we find your cousin Mabon?'

'You have done me a service, lord,' said Eidoel, 'and I shall do you another. I do not know where Mabon is, only that he was stolen from his mother when he was but three nights old, yet I shall seek news of him until I can tell you what you would know. It were well if first I asked of him from the animals and the birds—indeed, from the oldest bird of all, the Ouzel of Kilgwri.'

'Then let Gwrhyr the Interpreter go with you, for he knows the speech of beasts. And Kei, do you and Bedwyr go with them,' said Arthur.

So the four went to the old Ouzel of Kilgwri and Gwrhyr asked her, 'Where may we find Mabon, son of Modron?'

'When I first came to this spot,' replied the Ouzel, 'I was a young bird. There was a smith's anvil that stood here, and from that day to this no work has been done on that anvil save that I cleaned my beak upon it every evening; and now there is nothing remaining of the anvil save a piece the size of a hazel-nut, so long have I dwelt here. Yet in all that time I have heard no word of Mabon, son of Modron. But I would willingly help men who come from Arthur. There is a beast older than I; come with me to him and ask of Mabon.'

She led them to the Stag of Redynvre, but he said, 'When I first came to this place, there were no trees here save only one oak sapling which grew into a tree with one hundred branches. That tree has now grown old and withered, naught remains of it but a stump; yet in all that time I have never heard of Mabon, son of Modron. But there is a beast who is older than I; come with me to him, for I would gladly help Arthur's men.'

They went together to the Owl of Cwm Cawlwyd, but the Owl said, 'When I first came to this place a wood stretched here, as far as you can see. Men came and rooted up the trees; but when the men were gone, a second wood grew up. These trees which you see today, they are the third wood to stand here. Look at my wings, the feathers are gone, they are but stumps, so long have I lived here; yet in all that time I have never heard of Mabon, son of Modron. But I would help men who come from Arthur. There is a beast older than I; come with me to him.'

So they went to the Eagle of Gwern Abwy, but the Eagle said, 'When I first came to this place, this hill on which I perch was so high that, from its peak, each evening I could peck at the stars. Yet now you see that it stands no higher than a hand's breadth, so many years have worn away the hard rock. Yet in all that time I have never heard of Mabon, son of Modron, save only once when I went to Llyn Llyw and caught a salmon in the lake. I took him in my claws and would have flown off with him, but he dragged me down into the water, so that I hardly escaped alive. After that it was war between my folk and his, until we at last made peace. If he cannot tell you where to find Mabon, son of Modron, then I know not who can. But I will gladly take you to him.'

They went to the Salmon of Llyn Llyw and the Eagle asked him what he knew of Mabon, son of Modron. 'All I know I will tell you,' said the Salmon. 'With every tide I swim up the River Severn as far as the city of Gloucester, and there behind the walls of the prison I hear such wailing and lamenting as I have never heard in any other place. If you would hear it for yourselves, let two of you mount on my back and I will take you there.'

Kei and Gwrhyr the Interpreter climbed on to the Salmon's back and he swam with them up the Severn as far as the walls of Gloucester. And there, from the prison, they heard, as the Salmon had said, a great wailing and lamenting.

'Who is that who weeps in this house of stone?' called Gwrhyr.

From within the prison a voice answered him, 'It is I, Mabon, son of Modron, and I have reason enough to weep. No captivity was ever so long or so hard as mine.'

'Is there any hope that you may be ransomed for gold or silver? Or must it be by fighting that you are freed?'

'Whatever good comes to me will come through fighting alone,' replied Mabon.

At this they returned to Arthur and told him what they had learnt, and Arthur set out for Gloucester with his men. While Arthur laid siege to the castle, Kei and Bedwyr were carried up the river by the

Salmon to the prison walls; and Kei broke through the walls and brought Mabon out to safety while his gaolers were busy fighting Arthur. Then Arthur called off the siege, and they all returned in triumph to his court, accompanied by Mabon.

After that Arthur went with his men to seek the two whelps of the bitch Rhymi, and he found Rhymi in a cave, in the shape of a she-wolf, preying on men's cattle. They surrounded the place where she was hiding, drew in on her, and so caught the two young hounds.

Next, and quite unexpectedly, the flax seed sown by Hawthorn the Chief Giant was recovered, and this was the manner of it: one day, as Gwythyr, son of Greidawl, was walking on a mountain, he heard an outcry and a lamentation close by. He hastened to see what was amiss and found an anthill in flames. He drew his sword and cut off the top of the anthill, and so prevented the fire from spreading downwards and destroying the ants.

'Blessings on you for your kindness,' said the ants. 'That task which no man can perform, we shall perform for you in return.' And off they went to the field of the Chief Giant and quickly collected from the earth every single flax seed—save one—of the eighteen bushels that were lost, so that it might be planted in fresh land, that Olwen might have her wedding veil, as her father had demanded. And the one remaining flax seed, that also was brought in, late in the evening, by a lame ant which could not hurry.

Soon after, one day as Kei and Bedwyr were sitting on the top of Plinlimmon, they saw a great smoke to the south. Though the wind was blowing mightily, the smoke did not move in the wind, but went straight upwards, like a pillar. 'By the hand of my friend,' said Kei, 'that will be the fire of a mighty fighter,' and they came down from the mountain to look. When they came near to the smoke they saw that it was the giant Dillus the Bearded—the one warrior whom even Arthur did not care to meet—singeing the bristles from a boar he had killed.

'The luck is with us,' said Kei, 'for there is the beard we need to fashion a leash to hold the two whelps of Rhymi. But we must pluck it from him while he lives, remember. Let us wait until he has eaten, for then, perhaps, he will sleep.'

So they waited while Dillus cooked and ate his boar; and while they waited, they fashioned a pair of wooden tweezers. As soon as Dillus was asleep and snoring, they crept close quietly and dug a deep pit beneath his feet. Then Kei gave him a great blow and toppled him into the pit, and there he stayed, stuck fast with his head showing above the ground, unable to get out or to defend himself. Then they plucked out his beard, hair by hair, with the tweezers; and after that, for good measure, they killed him. Then, rejoicing and in high spirits, they returned to Arthur and gave him the leash they had plaited from the hairs.

Arthur laughed when he heard how cunningly Kei had tricked the giant, and in his mirth he made a verse of it:

> Our Kei has made a leash
> From the beard of Dillus, Eurei's son.
> Oh, Kei! If he still lived,
> Your days were quickly done.

Kei was so angry when he heard this verse that it was all Arthur's warriors could do to make peace between him and their lord. And even when the quarrel was over Kei refused to help further with the quests.

A little time before this happened, Gwythyr, son of Greidawl, the young chieftain whose kindness to the ants had solved for Arthur the problem of Hawthorn's flax field, had been betrothed to a fair maiden named Creidylad, the daughter of Lludd; but before the wedding had taken place, Gwyn, son of Nudd, had come and carried her off by force. Gwythyr had immediately gathered together his warriors and gone after them. But Gwyn and his followers had overcome Gwythyr and his men and had taken many captives. When Arthur heard of this, he was angry, and with his army he now marched to the north and demanded that Gwyn should set free his prisoners. This was done, and they returned to their homes. But because he could in no way settle the rivalry between the two young chieftains for the hand of Creidylad, Arthur declared that she was to be the wife of neither, but that she was to go back to her father's house and that, every year on the first of May, Gwyn and Gwythyr should fight for her, from that very year until the end of the world; and when that day finally came, he who was then the victor should have Creidylad. After this had been settled, Arthur returned to his court, and with him rode Gwyn, son of Nudd, and Gwythyr, son of Greidawl, to help in the quest for the bride-price for Olwen.

Then Arthur set himself to find the other treasures demanded by Hawthorn the Chief Giant, and, after much seeking and much fighting in Ireland and Brittany and in the north of Britain, he had obtained the horse Gwyn Baymane, the hounds Aned and Aethlem, the leash of Cors of the Hundred Claws, the collar of Canhastyr of the Hundred Hands and the chain of Kilydd of the Hundred Holds, and the hound Drudwyn himself; and had achieved many other marvels. Then, mounted on Llamrei, Arthur's mare, Cado of North Britain killed Whitetusk the Chief Boar and took charge of his tusk, with which Hawthorn was to be shaved.

Arthur and the others were well pleased by their success, and Kilhwch more than any, as he saw the day of his marriage draw nearer. But there still remained a task or two, and amongst them the hardest task of all, the hunting of the enchanted boar Trwyth, who had once been a man and a king, and the taking of his comb and shears.

'First,' said Arthur, 'it is best that we make certain that Trwyth still has his comb and shears. It would be folly to waste our labours.' He bade Menw the Sorcerer find out, and Menw went to Ireland, where Trwyth was laying waste the countryside. In the shape of a bird Menw spied upon Trwyth in his lair, and saw that the comb and the shears did indeed still lie between the ears of the giant boar. At the sight of them, Menw boldly flew down and swooped upon the boar and tried to seize one of the treasures in his beak. But all he succeeded in snatching was a single bristle. The plucking out of his bristle made Trwyth so angry that he rose and shook himself, glaring about him. As he shook himself, some drops of his sweat and his spittle splashed upon Menw, who never had his full health from that day on.

Having learnt that the comb and the shears were still there for the taking, Arthur gathered together his army and all the men who were to hunt Trwyth, with the marvels they needed for the hunt, and he sailed to Ireland. The Irish were not sorry to see him come, for they hoped that he might deliver their land from the ravages of the giant boar. But first Arthur won the cauldron of Diurnach the Irishman, in which to boil the meat for Olwen's wedding feast; and then he and his men sought out the boar Trwyth. Arthur's men fought with the boar and his seven young pigs all one day, but gained no advantage. The next day it was the same; and then, on the third day, Arthur himself attacked the boar. For nine days and nine nights Arthur fought him; and yet at the end of that time, he had not killed even a single one of the seven young pigs.

Then Arthur bade Gwrhyr the Interpreter go to speak with Trwyth. Like Menw, Gwrhyr changed himself into a bird and flew to the lair of the boar, and alighting above the opening, he called out, 'Let one of your sons come out to parley with Arthur.'

One of the young pigs, Grugyn of the Silver Bristles, answered him. 'Why should we speak to Arthur? And why should he come to molest us?'

'Arthur has come to take the comb and the shears which are between the ears of Trwyth.'

'He shall never have them while Trwyth lives,' replied Silver Bristles. 'And moreover, tell Arthur that tomorrow we shall rise up and go into his own land, and lay it waste, even as we have laid waste Ireland.'

It was indeed as he had said; for the next day the boar Trwyth and his seven young pigs swam across the sea to Wales. After them sailed Arthur and his men. In Wales Trwyth slew men and cattle; and Arthur, with his army and his huntsmen, and with the hounds Drudwyn and Aned and Aethlem, and the two whelps of the bitch Rhymi, and with Caval his own hound, also, who was in the charge of Bedwyr—with all these and more—Arthur began the great hunt across all Wales. The boar and the young pigs went before them, every here and there turning at bay, each time slaying many famed warriors. And then, for a time, Trwyth evaded his pursuers, and no man knew where he was hidden.

Certain huntsmen followed the tracks of the seven young pigs, while Arthur and the army came after them, keeping a look-out for Trwyth. But, in a wild place, the two mightiest of the young pigs, Grugyn of the Silver Bristles and Llwydawg the Hewer, broke cover and rushed at the huntsmen, killing all but one who escaped to tell Arthur.

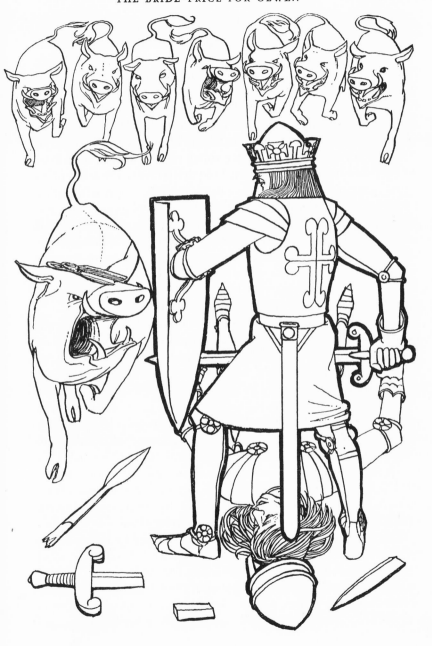

When Arthur heard what had happened, he hurried onwards and set all the hounds on the triumphant pigs. What with the shouts of the men, the baying of the hounds and the grunts and squeals of Silver Bristles and the Hewer, the clamour reached to Trwyth, and he came to the help of his sons. At once every man and hound turned to attack him, but he fought his way through them and led his seven young pigs to safety, as far as Mynydd Amanw. And there the first of the young pigs was slain. With the great host after him, Trwyth made for Dyffryn Amanw, and on the way two more young pigs were slain. At Dyffryn Amanw died two more; and when Trwyth left Dyffryn Amanw, of his seven young pigs he had but Silver Bristles and the Hewer left. Farther on he made another stand against his pursuers, slaying many men and hounds. Then Silver Bristles parted from his father and his brother and sought to escape alone; but he was followed by certain of Arthur's men and finally slain; yet not before he had wrought great havoc amongst his enemies. The remainder of Arthur's men followed Trwyth and the Hewer; and, at great cost, the Hewer was slain, so that only Trwyth himself was left; and he made towards Cornwall.

Then Arthur gathered about him all his remaining men and hounds and he said, 'The boar Trwyth has laid waste much of my land and slain many of my men. Yet he shall not go into Cornwall to do likewise there.' And he spread out his men like a net to drive Trwyth back towards the River Severn.

So many there were opposed to him, that the great boar was driven into the waters of the river; and even into the river was he pursued by Mabon, son of Modron, riding on Gwyn Baymane; and with Mabon were Goreu, the son of Custennin, and Menw the Sorcerer, and Osla of the Big Knife. These four seized hold of Trwyth by the legs and tried to drown him in the river, while they snatched the shears from between his ears. But before they could take the comb as well, Trwyth had flung them off and was making for the river's bank.

In the struggle, Osla of the Big Knife had dropped his knife into the river, and now, dragged down by the weight of the water that filled its empty sheath, he was all but drowned and had to be dragged to land by his companions; so that in the confusion Trwyth escaped them. Once on the land again, neither man nor horse nor swift hound could overtake the boar until he had reached Cornwall. There Arthur and his men came up with him; and where they had had trouble before, in winning the shears, they had even more trouble now, in winning the comb. Yet at last, with great labour and much loss of men and hounds, the comb was taken, and Trwyth was driven into the sea. After him swam the two hounds Aned and Aethlem; and none of the three was ever seen again.

'Is any one of the tasks yet unfulfilled?' asked Arthur.

'Only the blood of the Black Witch, daughter of the White Witch, lord,' he was answered.

So once again Arthur and his men went into the north and came to the Black Witch's cave. At the counsel of Gwyn, son of Nudd, two strong warriors were sent alone into the cave to fetch her out. But she caught up one of them by the hair and flung him to the ground; and when the other would have dragged her off his companion, she kicked them both, bruised and bleeding, out of her cave.

Arthur, mightily angry to see this, would have entered the cave himself, but Gwyn and his rival Gwythyr prevented him, saying, 'It would not be fitting that Arthur should fall to fighting with a hag.' And they persuaded him to send in two more warriors.

But if the first pair had had pains and torments in plenty, the second pair fared far worse; and out they were thrown, so that they were hardly able to crawl back to their comrades. And all four of them had to be laid across the back of Arthur's mare, Llamrei, and carried away like sacks of chaff.

At this sorry sight Arthur was so furious that he did not stay for anyone's counsel, but ran to the opening of the cave and struck out with his sword and cut the Black Witch in two halves, right through her middle; and Cado collected her blood in two pails for the shaving of Hawthorn the Chief Giant.

Then, all the tasks having been accomplished, the bride-price for Olwen could be paid, and Kilhwch set off for the Chief Giant's castle. With him went Goreu, the son of Custennin, and Cado of North Britain with the tusk of the Chief Boar and the blood of the Black Witch, and their followers carrying all the marvels they had won.

'You rogues of servants, prop open my eyes, that I may see my son-in-law,' shouted Hawthorn the Chief Giant. 'Have you brought the bride-price for my daughter?' he demanded.

'We have,' they answered him.

Then, with the blood of the Black Witch and the tusk of the Chief Boar, Cado shaved Hawthorn's beard—and not only his beard, but his skin and his flesh to the very bone, and his two ears as well.

'Are you shaved now?' laughed Kilhwch.

'Alas! I am shaved,' answered Hawthorn.

'Is your daughter Olwen mine now?'

'She is yours. But you have no need to thank me for it, since I would never have given her to you of my own will. Thank Arthur who has brought this to pass for you. Now make haste, for it is time for me to die.'

Then Goreu took his uncle the Chief Giant by the hair of his head and dragged him out from the hall, struck off his head and set it on a stake on the wall. And so the deaths of his three and twenty brothers, and the sufferings of his mother and his father Custennin, were avenged at last.

That very day Kilhwch and Olwen were married, and she was his beloved wife for as long as she lived. After the marriage feasting, all Arthur's warriors dispersed and went each man to his own lands. And thus, in fulfilment of the destiny which had been laid upon him by his stepmother, did Kilhwch win for his wife Olwen, daughter of Hawthorn the Chief Giant.

★   ★   ★

The cauldron of plenty is a very popular element in Celtic myth. There is the cauldron of the Dagda, from which no one was turned away unsatisfied; the cauldron that made the dead alive, which Bran gave to Matholwch of Ireland when he married Bran's sister, Branwen; and in this last story we have both the cauldron of Diurnach the Irishman and the mwys—'receptacle'—of Gwyddno of the Long Legs. Pwyll and his son Pryderi, gods of the underworld, owned a cauldron set with pearls around its edge, which would not cook the food of a coward or a perjurer. In an early and rather obscure Welsh poem, ascribed to Taliesin, is described how Arthur and his companions invaded the domain of Pwyll and carried off his cauldron. Pwyll is the original of the King Pelles of the later Arthurian romances; and by that time his cauldron has become the Holy Grail which is sought by Arthur's knights.

The everlasting combat between Gwyn—representing winter and darkness

—and Gwythyr—representing summer and light—for the possession of Creidylad—the spring with all its flowers and growing crops—is an obvious nature myth. In this story, as in others, Creidylad is the daughter of Lludd, the sky-god; but another tradition makes her the daughter of the sea-god Llyr; and as Cordeilla, daughter of King Leir of Britain, she appears in the Historia Regum Britanniae *of Geoffrey of Monmouth; and it was from the pages of Geoffrey that Shakespeare took the plot for his* King Lear.

5

THE PURSUIT OF THE HARD MAN

The stories about Finn Mac Cool belong to a later legendary cycle than the two previous Irish stories in this book. There are a great many tales connected with Finn and his followers, and this is not surprising, since he is the best-loved hero of the Gaelic-speaking peoples—in Scotland and the Isle of Man, as well as in Ireland.

Finn Mac Cool—who is unlikely to have been a real historical figure, in spite of many theories to this effect—and his men of the Fianna formed a standing army of well-tried warriors who could be called upon by the High King of Ireland to defend the land for him in times of danger; and when Finn and his friends were not fighting, they were hunting. Many of his adventures begin with the words: 'When Finn and the Fianna were hunting in. . . .' The two following stories are of this kind.

The first one is light and cheerful, and not very serious.

*   *   *

Every year, so long as Ireland was at peace, from the beginning of May to the end of October, the Fianna would hunt each day with their hounds, going here and there all about Ireland in search of deer and boar. One year, when they were on their first hunt of the summer, Finn and a few of his companions—amongst them were Oisin, his son, red-haired Oscar, his grandson, Gaul Mac Morna, Fergus Finnvel, the poet, Conan the Bald, and Finn's nephew, handsome, auburn-haired Dermot O'Dyna—sat down to rest from the chase on the top of the hill of Knockainy, in Limerick. Finn was ever fond of a game of chess, so they set out the chessboard and the men on the green grass, and he began a game with one of the others, while Finn Ban Mac Bresal stood a short way off and kept watch.

The game had only been started a little time when Finn Ban came running back towards them, calling out excitedly, and they all jumped to their feet.

'There is a giant coming this way, leading a horse,' he cried.

They looked and saw the giant leading a horse, even as Finn Ban had said—but what a sight he was, quite the ugliest giant any one of them had ever seen. He was pot-bellied and knock-kneed, with huge, flat feet that turned inwards as he walked, and, set on the top of a scraggy neck, he had a thick-lipped, yellow-toothed, shock-haired head. A big rusty sword was slung about him and with one hand he was carrying two rusty iron spears and dragging behind him a huge iron club which left a track as broad as the track of a plough. With the other hand he pulled at the halter of his horse. And if the giant was ugly, his horse was no better. It was huge and gaunt, with all its ribs showing through its shaggy hide, a head which seemed to be all jaws, and jaws which were full of great yellow teeth. It seemed to be a stubborn beast, too, with a will of its own; for every now and then it would stand stock-still, with all four clumsy hooves planted firmly on the ground, and refuse to move until the giant had struck it a blow with his club and had hauled on the rope fit to pull off its head. And every so often it would give a tug at the halter in its turn, so that the giant was dragged backwards until his arm was all but torn from his shoulder. Yet neither of this strange pair seemed in the least perturbed by the other's tricks, and slowly they approached Finn and his friends, who watched them in astonishment.

When he had reached them, the giant bent his head and dropped on one knee and greeted Finn. Finn greeted him in return and asked him his name and his ancestry, his country and his craft.

'Finn,' answered the giant, 'I cannot tell you my ancestry, for I do not know who my parents were. I come from the north and I travel through all the world, serving any master who will pay me for my service. I heard tell of Finn Mac Cool as a good man to serve, so I have come to find you, and, if you are willing, I would take service with you for a year and a day. As for my name: I am called the Gilla Dacker—the Hard Man—for I am a hard fellow to bear with at all times. I am lazy and I grumble all day; however well I am treated I am ungrateful and ill-spoken; and as for food—I usually eat as much as would be enough for a hundred ordinary men.'

Finn laughed. 'Truly, on your own recommendation you must be a sore trial to any master. But I have never yet refused a man who offered to serve me, so I will take you into my service for a year and a day.'

At this the giant turned to Conan the Bald and asked him, 'In the service of Finn Mac Cool, who gets the higher wage, a horseman or a man on foot?'

'A horseman gets twice the pay of a man on foot,' replied Conan.

'In that case,' said the Hard Man, 'I will be a horseman, seeing that I have a horse of my own. Indeed, had I known it before, I would have ridden up the hill in fine style instead of walking. But since I can see no one here who looks fit to care for my horse, I suppose I shall have to groom him myself, for he is a good horse and I would not want him neglected. And since I think highly of him and would not have him come to harm, I put him under your protection, Finn, and under the protection of all the Fianna.'

There was much laughter at this, and no one laughed more loudly or longer than Conan the Bald. But the Hard Man paid no heed, he merely took the halter from his horse and turned it loose amongst the horses of the Fianna which were grazing close by.

As soon as the horse was free, it began to attack the other horses, kicking them and biting them and teasing them, until there was not a single horse which had not been hurt in some way. The horses of Conan the Bald were grazing by themselves, a little way off, and when it had done what harm it could to the horses of Finn and the others, the ugly horse of the Hard Man made straight for Conan's horses.

At once Conan was thrown into a fine flurry and rushed about, trying to head off the horse, shouting all the time to the Hard Man to tie it up; and threatening to kill the wretched animal if he could not prevent it in any other way from savaging his own horses.

The Hard Man seemed unmoved and only shrugged his shoulders. 'If you put the halter on him, it will stop him. But it seems cruel not to let him graze in peace. However, here is the halter if you want it.' And he tossed it at Conan.

Conan was ill pleased at being made to act as a groom, but he snatched up the halter and went after the big horse and threw it over its head. The horse immediately stood still, and all Conan's tugging and pulling could not budge it an inch. Conan cursed it and grew more angry every second, yet he dared not let go of the halter, for fear that the horse would run away and attack his own horses.

Watching him, Finn and the Fianna laughed heartily; and Fergus Finnvel, the poet, said, 'Never did I think, Conan, that I would live to see the day when you played horseboy to any man, least of all to an ugly giant from the north and his hideous nag. But here is a word of advice: stop cursing the brute and get on his back instead. Why do you not ride him up and down a few rocky hillsides and in and out of a few bogs, until you have broken his heart for him and avenged yourself for all the trouble he has given you?'

Conan stopped his cursing and jumped on the horse's back, but though he kicked it and hammered at it with his fists, the horse paid no heed.

'I can guess what is wrong, Conan,' laughed Fergus. 'Fat though you may be, you are not as heavy as the stranger. The brute is used to carrying the Hard Man, you do not weigh enough.'

'Then let some of you mount with me, and avenge the damage done to your horses,' said Conan furiously.

'Here I come,' laughed Coil Croda, and he jumped up behind Conan. But still the horse would not move.

Then up jumped Dara Donn Mac Morna and Angus Art Mac Morna, and after them several others, until there were in all fifteen men of the Fianna sitting on the horse's back—and very uncomfortable they were, perched on the ridge of its sharp and bony spine—but still it would not move.

Though the rest of the Fianna who were looking on were laughing until they had to wipe away the tears at the sorry spectacle of their comrades on the hideous horse, the Hard Man suddenly seemed to grow angry. 'Finn Mac Cool,' he said, 'I see well that all the fine tales that I have heard of you and the Fianna are naught but lies, if this is the way you treat my good horse. I have been in your service but a very short time, yet it seems too long to me. Pay me my wages and let me go.'

'I will pay you at the end of the year,' said Finn, 'and not before.'

'Wages or no wages, I am going today. And wherever I go, there shall I tell the truth about Finn Mac Cool and the Fianna.' And off the Hard Man went, his head high and his chin in the air. And after him went his horse, the fifteen men of the Fianna on its back. The others gave a mocking cheer, as they saw the horse move at last; but the Hard Man began to lope away at a great pace down the hill and across the plain, and the horse began to gallop after him. The fifteen men tried to dismount, but found they were stuck fast and quite unable to move, and they shouted to Finn for help, with Conan shouting the loudest of all.

'After them,' cried Finn, and he and the others ran down the hill, with Liagan, one of the swiftest of the Fianna—though he was not as swift as Keelta Mac Ronan—at their head.

Right across the country went the Hard Man and his horse, until they came to the sea, and there, as they paused a brief moment, Liagan caught up with the horse and took hold of its tail to hold it back. But the horse galloped straight into the sea, dragging Liagan with it; and when Liagan tried to let go of its tail, he found that he, too, was stuck fast and had to hold on and be towed behind through the waves.

Finn and the others stood helplessly on the shore, watching the Hard Man and his horse swim out of sight, bearing sixteen of the Fianna with them.

After a time Finn spoke to the others. 'What do you all counsel that we should do?'

'It is you who are wiser than we, Finn,' they replied. 'We shall do whatever you think best.'

Fergus Finnvel the poet said, 'If you would know what I think best, lord, it is that we should find a ship as soon as we may, and sail over the sea after the giant and his horse.'

'That is my advice, too,' said Finn.

They were about to set off in search of a ship, when they saw two fine young warriors approaching over the sands, both armed and wearing scarlet cloaks. They greeted Finn, and he greeted them in return and asked their names.

'I am Feradach and this is my brother Foltlor, and we are the two sons of a king. Each of us has a skill and we have long disputed as to which of us has the more useful skill, each claiming his own to be the better. Now we have come, Finn Mac Cool, to ask if you will take us into your service for a year, that you may, in your wisdom, tell us at the end of that time which one of us is right.'

'What are your skills?' asked Finn.

'I,' replied Feradach, 'have this skill: if ever there is need of a ship, with only my sling for casting stones and my axe, I can make a ship by striking my sling three blows with my axe, so long as all present will cover their eyes and not watch me while I do so.'

'And I,' said Foltlor, 'have this skill: I can follow any track, whether on land or sea, without losing it.'

Finn smiled. 'You have brought me your skills at the moment when I most need them. Gladly will I take you both into my service for a year from this very day.' And he told them the adventure of the Hard Man and his horse and of the loss of his companions. 'Now, my friends, make me a ship that will carry us after them, and guide it without error through the sea.'

'That can we do for you,' answered the brothers. And in the very manner in which he had told them that he could, Feradach made them a ship.

Finn picked out fifteen men to go with him on his quest; among them were Gaul Mac Morna, Dermot O'Dyna, Oscar, his grandson, Fergus Finnvel the poet, and the brothers Feradach and Foltlor; and he left his son Oisin in charge of the Fianna, to guard Ireland for him until his return. Then those who were to go entered the ship which Feradach had made, and with Foltlor to steer them, they set off across the sea on the trail of the Hard Man and his horse.

For many days they sailed, through sunshine and through storm, over calm water and over rough waves, until they reached land, and there the track of the Hard Man led them to the foot of a high cliff.

For a long time they were all silent, staring at the cliff and wondering how they might climb it. Then Fergus said drily, 'On the top of that cliff are no doubt our comrades, and who knows what torments they may be suffering. I am a poet and I have no skill save in the making of verses; but we have one with us who is famed for his skill in all manly feats, and who has, moreover, learnt much from his foster-father, Angus of the Birds. With a god for foster-father, it is strange that he does not try to climb that cliff and find out what has befallen his friends.'

At his words Dermot O'Dyna flushed with anger. 'I know that it is of me you speak, Fergus,' he said. Goaded, he rose, and taking up his two spears, one in each hand, he vaulted with their aid high up the face of the cliff and found a foothold on a ledge. From there he slowly climbed higher and yet higher, finding here a foothold and there a grip for his hands, while the others watched him anxiously until at last he reached the top, and with a glance of farewell towards his comrades, standing a long way below, he walked onwards, out of their sight.

At the top of the cliff he found himself in a fair, green land with birds singing, bees buzzing in the many-coloured flowers, and trees of every kind. Before long he came to a clear spring and a pool beneath a tall tree. Beside the pool was a pillar-stone, and surrounding tree and pool and pillar-stone was a ring of smaller stones. By this time Dermot was thirsty and he was glad to see the water. Kneeling beside it he bent his head to drink. Immediately he did so, he heard the sound as of an army all about him. He leapt to his feet—but he was alone. Puzzled, he stooped again to drink, and immediately he heard once more the clang of arms and the neighing of horses and the sound of chariot wheels. Again he jumped up, but, as before, there was no one there beside himself. Bewildered, he gazed around him, and then he saw, on the top of the pillar-stone beside the pool, a golden drinking-horn set with gems, and he smiled to himself. 'Without a doubt it is not permitted to drink from this pool save by means of that horn,' he thought. Taking the horn, he filled it at the spring and was at once able to drink as much as he wished without interruption.

But as soon as he had replaced the drinking-horn upon the pillar-stone, he saw approaching a tall warrior clothed in red and gold. This warrior stepped into the ring of stones and cried out angrily, 'Have you not water enough in Ireland, Dermot O'Dyna, that you must come into my land and drink from my spring, out of my drinking-horn, without leave? You shall pay dearly for your insolence.' With that he drew his sword and ran at Dermot. But Dermot was ready for him, and met him with his own sword; and so began a fight between two well-matched warriors which lasted all the day without either gaining the advantage. Then, at sunset, the stranger suddenly gave a leap and vanished into the depths of the pool.

Perplexed and provoked by this ending to the combat, Dermot stood beside the pool and looked down into the water. But nothing could he discern in its dark depths; so finally he shrugged his shoulders and turned away, meaning to sleep beside the spring that night and see what the next day brought. Suddenly he caught sight of a herd of deer a short way off, and realizing how hungry he was, he took aim at one with his spear and killed it. He then built a fire, and having skinned and roasted the deer, he sat beside his fire eating his supper and drinking water from the spring in the golden drinking-horn. After that he lay down beneath the tall tree and slept undisturbed until the dawn.

With the sunrise he went in search of another deer, and coming upon the herd again, he killed one and cooked and ate it as before, and drank water from the spring. When he had replaced the drinking-horn on the pillar-stone, he turned and saw the strange warrior standing near by. And if the stranger had been angry the day before, that morning he was far more angry.

'Dermot O'Dyna,' he cried, 'not content with drinking the water of my spring out of my drinking-horn, you have slain two of my deer and eaten them. Have you no deer of your own in Ireland that you need to take mine? You escaped my just wrath yesterday, but today you shall pay in full for your rashness.' And with that he attacked Dermot, who was, as before, ready for him and parried his stroke.

All that day they fought without either gaining the advantage; and in the evening it happened again that the stranger leapt into the pool and sank out of sight. That night, also, Dermot slept under the tree and in the morning he broke his fast off deer's flesh and water from the spring. As before the warrior appeared and they fought fiercely all that day. But as evening drew close, Dermot watched his adversary carefully, and at the moment that the stranger made to leap into the pool, Dermot leapt also and caught hold of him, and down through the water they both went, clinging fast to each other. Dermot tried to see where he was going, but all around him was darkness; until at last there appeared a faint gleam of light, and then suddenly they were in full daylight, standing on green grass in a land even fairer than that which they had just left.

At the second that they reached the ground, the stranger tore himself from Dermot's grasp and ran away towards a fortress that stood near by within a wall, outside which were a number of warriors practising feats of arms. Dermot ran after him, but the stranger reached the group of warriors and they stood aside for him so that he went on safely into the stronghold. Yet when Dermot came up to them, the warriors closed their ranks against him, and a long, hard fight he had before they were all scattered and fled.

Wounded and dispirited, Dermot looked about him and saw no one else in sight. Before him were the closed gates of the stronghold, and behind him and to each side was the pleasant, flowered, green plain. And for all his pains and labour he seemed to be no nearer finding the Hard Man or his comrades of the Fianna. Then a great weariness came over him from all his fighting and he lay down where he was, caring nothing for his enemies, and fell into a deep sleep.

He was awake on an instant when someone struck him a light blow with the flat of a sword, and he jumped to his feet, seizing his weapons, to see standing by him a tall young man with golden hair.

The young man smiled. 'Put up your sword, Dermot O'Dyna, for I am a friend. I did but waken you when I found you sleeping so rashly before the walls of your enemies. Come with me and I can offer you a soft bed and better entertainment than you could find out here on the plain.'

Dermot liked the appearance of the young man, so he thanked him and went willingly with him. After a while they came to a fine, large house, where they were greeted by a company of warriors and fair women, all richly clad in scarlet, and with golden hair. Some were playing chess and others were listening to the music of harps.

In this house Dermot bathed and refreshed himself, and his many wounds were healed in an instant with sweet-smelling herbs; then, clad in rich garments like theirs, he joined the gay company in the hall and they feasted together. After the feasting they slept; and in the morning Dermot questioned his host, asking the name of the land in which he now found himself.

'This is Underwater Land,' said the young man. 'My brother is its king. It was he with whom you fought at the spring. Rightfully, half of the kingdom should be mine, but my brother has stolen my heritage from me and so I live in this house with my few faithful friends about me, longing for the day when I can take up arms and win back what is mine. Now that you have come here, I am ready to dare battle against my brother; for with you to fight for me I could not fail to be victorious. Of all the men of the Fianna, I would rather have you at my side than any other. Dermot O'Dyna, will you help me regain my birthright?'

'Most willingly,' said Dermot; and taking hands, he and his host pledged friendship. Immediately they made ready for war, and as soon as their preparations were completed, they attacked the stronghold on the plain; and before many days' fighting were done, with Dermot's help the king of Underwater Land was slain and his army defeated, and his brother was king in his place.

Meanwhile, at the foot of the cliff Finn and the others waited. When several days had passed and Dermot had not returned, they determined to go after him, yet they did not know how to climb the cliff. At last an idea came to them and Feradach and Foltlor cut all the ropes from the ship's rigging, and knotting them together, made a rope long enough to stretch from top to bottom of the cliff. Then, with great pain and trouble, they succeeded in climbing to the top, carrying the rope with them. At the top they made it fast to a steady rock, and Finn and the men of the Fianna climbed up by means of it.

When they all stood together at the top of the cliff, they were gladdened, as Dermot had been, by the fair land which stretched before them. Foltlor easily found Dermot's tracks and they followed them to the spring and there they saw the ashes of his fire, the remains of his meals, and all the signs of a fierce combat.

'Alas,' said Finn, 'I fear that Dermot is slain or captured.'

While they were standing there sadly, they saw a horseman approaching. He was a handsome man with a majestic and noble manner, richly clad. He greeted them by name, declaring that their fame had reached even to his country, and he bade them come with him to his house near by for rest and entertainment.

The best of food and drink, with good songs to hear, were their lot in his fine house; and after the feasting he told them all that they asked him concerning his land and himself. The land, he told them, was called the land of Sorca, and he was its king. He then questioned Finn, asking why he was so far from Ireland; and Finn told him how he and his companions were searching for the Hard Man, who had stolen away sixteen of their comrades, and how they had lost Dermot, whom they believed slain.

'I have never heard of the Hard Man,' said the king of Sorca. 'But you seem to me to be on a dangerous quest, my friends, and one for which you are too few. If you permit it, I shall send warriors of my own with you, to be under your command and serve you in what way you will.'

But before Finn could even thank him for his offer, a messenger hastened into the hall with word of a huge army which had invaded the land from over the sea. 'Their ships, lord,' he said to the king, 'cover the water as far as the eye can see. They are more than the stars in the sky or the leaves of the forest, more even than the sands on the shore. And already some of the enemy are disembarked and ravaging the coast. It is said that it is he who calls himself the King of the World, come to conquer us as he has conquered so many other lands.'

The king of Sorca was greatly distressed when he heard this, and could find nothing to say. But Finn, remembering his host's kindness of a few moments before, leapt to his feet and said, 'What I and my few men can do to help you, we shall do willingly.' And the king of Sorca took heart, that he had even only a few men of the famed Fianna to fight for him, and he called together his army and made ready for war. Then he and Finn marched against the invaders where they were encamped on the coast; and after many days of fierce fighting, they had slain so many enemy warriors that the King of the World abandoned his undertaking and sailed for home.

Hardly had they had time to rejoice at this, when they saw a band of armed men approaching, led by a tall, proud warrior. At first they feared that here might be another enemy coming to attack them; then Finn recognized the leader. 'It is Dermot!' he cried in joy; and he and the men of the Fianna ran forward to embrace him.

Eagerly Dermot told them of his adventures since he had parted from them; and they told him of theirs.

'And I have yet further news,' said Dermot. 'The king of Underwater Land, with the aid of magical powers, has learnt that the Hard Man is no other than Avarta the enchanter, and that our sixteen comrades are held captive in the Land of Promise.'

After consultation together, Finn and the others decided that they would go back to the top of the cliff—where they had turned aside from tracking the Hard Man, to go in search of Dermot—and let Foltlor pick up the trail of the Hard Man once more, so that they might follow it to its end in the Land of Promise. Though both the king of Sorca and the king of Underwater Land would have sent warriors with them to help them, Finn and the others were determined to go alone; and so they set off, after bidding their new friends farewell.

At the top of the cliff Foltlor soon found the tracks of the Hard Man, though not without difficulty, for the giant had taken great pains to cover all trace of the way he had gone, knowing as he did by this time that after him was coming Foltlor, who never failed to follow a track to its ending. And once again, in spite of the cunning of the Hard Man, Foltlor did not fail, but he kept to the track over land and water, from bay to bay and from island to island, until they came to the Land of Promise, where Dermot had been for a time, many years before, as a guest of Manannan Mac Lir, the sea-god.

'Now that we are here,' said Finn, 'let us lay waste the land in vengeance for the carrying off of our friends.'

'No,' said Dermot hastily, 'let us not do so, for the people of this land are skilled in magical arts and it is best not to anger them more than we need. Let us rather send a messenger to Avarta to demand the release of Conan and the others. If he refuses, then we can lay waste the land; but if he listens to our demands, so much the better.'

To this Finn agreed, and Foltlor and another warrior were sent to Avarta's house with Finn's message. Their surprise was great when they found the sixteen men of the Fianna, well and happy enough in their captivity, amusing themselves with games and feats of strength on the green plain before Avarta's house. The prisoners all called to Avarta to come out and speak with Finn's messengers, and he did so. Nothing like the Hard Man he looked now, but tall and straight and kingly. When he had heard Finn's words, he took counsel with his lords, and they advised him to set free the sixteen men of the Fianna and to meet with Finn as a friend.

To this Avarta agreed, and he prepared a feast for Finn and they clasped hands in friendship. For three days they feasted and on the fourth day they sat down to discuss the matter of satisfaction for the trick which Avarta had played on Finn.

'What do you demand in redress?' asked Avarta.

'I ask no redress,' replied Finn. 'Instead I will pay you the wage which I promised when you came to me in the guise of the Hard Man that day on Knockainy. And from this day on let there be peace and friendship between us.'

At this Conan the Bald jumped to his feet. 'It is well enough for you, Finn. What have you suffered in this matter? I was among those who were carried off and imprisoned; and even if you do not, I demand satisfaction from Avarta—as you would, too, had you been forced to endure a ride on the back of his monster horse.'

Avarta, smiling at the recollection of Conan and the others on the back of his horse, said, 'Name your satisfaction, Conan, and you shall get it. For I do not wish to arouse your tongue to foul jibing.'

When Finn and the rest heard this, they were afraid that greedy Conan might shame the Fianna by demanding great sums of gold and silver or suchlike treasure; but Conan said, 'My satisfaction shall be this, Avarta, that fifteen of your noblest men—and amongst them those who are your closest friends—shall mount on the back of your wretched horse and, with you holding to its tail, shall travel to Ireland in the same manner and by the same path that we were forced to take. Do this, and I shall have had satisfaction enough.'

To this Avarta agreed; and Finn and the Fianna at once set sail for Ireland to await his coming on the top of the hill of Knockainy.

And to them there came fifteen of the friends of Avarta, riding on the monster horse, with Avarta himself, once more in the shape of the Hard Man, running behind, holding to the beast's tail. All the Fianna burst out laughing at the sight and congratulated Conan on a well-chosen revenge.

Then the Hard Man came near and Finn went to greet him with courtesy; but the Hard Man stood up straight and tall, and pointing to a spot behind the Fianna, looked earnestly into the distance. Startled, Finn and the others turned to see what was amiss; yet all they could see were their own horses grazing quietly, and the plain beyond. But when they turned back again to the Hard Man, he was not there. Avarta the enchanter and his fifteen friends, and the hideous horse with them, had all vanished, leaving no trace, and they were never again seen in Ireland.

★　　★　　★

The tale of the Hard Man, in the version which we know today, is an example of how the details of a story can change in the course of the centuries through the retellings of storytellers and the errors and alterations of scribes. As we have it now, it is the story of a practical joke played on the Fianna by an enchanter; but it will undoubtedly have originally been a tale of a type that was very popular with the ancient storytellers: of the abduction or enticing away of a mortal hero or heroes, by an immortal who needs human help against his own immortal enemies. In the earliest versions of the story of The Pursuit of the Hard Man, *the king of Sorca, the king of Underwater Land, and Avarta—both as sorcerer and Hard Man—would all have been one and the same: the god who needed the help of the Fianna. As far as the episode of Dermot at the pool, the story is probably very little changed from the earliest versions; but after that the plot becomes confused, and the original point of the story is lost in all the separate adventures that have been welded into it.*

There are many allusions in ancient Irish literature to a marvellous land under the sea. In the stories in this book, as well as Underwater Land, there is the country beneath the waves seen by Maeldun during his voyage. Belief in these undersea countries probably springs from the universal acceptance of the tradition of the lost continent of Atlantis.

6

THE HOUSE OF THE ROWAN TREES

In the time of the people of Dana, there was a certain enchanted well in which swam a divine salmon. Around the well grew nine hazel trees whose crimson nuts, when ripe, fell into the water, where they were swallowed by the salmon. It was the property of these nuts that they gave knowledge of everything in the world to those who ate them; yet it was only the salmon in the well who might eat the hazel-nuts—not even the gods were permitted to taste them. But Boann, wife of the Dagda, was eager for knowledge of all things; so one day she went to the well to pick a nut for herself. As she did so, the water of the well rose upwards to engulf her for her presumption. She managed to escape the torrent that poured after her; but the water was unable to return to the well, and it flowed away and became the River Boyne with the Salmon of Knowledge swimming in it. Long after, by chance and all unsuspecting, Finn Mac Cool tasted the Salmon of Knowledge, thereby gaining great understanding.

The following adventure of Finn and the Fianna is of a rather more serious and heroic pattern than the last; though, once again, Conan the Bald provides a moment or two of humour.

The men of Lochlann, who figure as the enemies in so many of Finn's adventures, were probably the Norsemen.

*   *   *

In the days when Cormac Mac Art was High King of Ireland, a great warrior named Colga was king over Lochlann. One day Colga called together all his lords and chieftains, and sitting on his throne on the broad plain that stretched before his fortress, he spoke to them all.

'In the years that I have ruled over you,' he asked, 'have you found anything for which I may be blamed?'

With one voice they all replied that they had found nothing for which they blamed him.

'Then you do not judge as I judge,' said the king drily. 'I am called king of the tribes of Lochlann and ruler of the Islands of the Sea: yet there is one island which I do not rule.'

'What island is that?' they asked.

'Ireland of the green hills,' replied Colga. 'My forefathers fought bravely in Ireland. Indeed, for a time they conquered the land; but they were cast out and so today I do not rule in Ireland. This seems to me a fault in me. Therefore I would sail with an army to Ireland and conquer the Irish and rule them until the end of the world. How does this seem to you, my people?'

It seemed good to the men of Lochlann that they should conquer Ireland, so Colga made ready with men and weapons and white-sailed ships; and when everything was prepared, he set forth with his lords and warriors, taking with him all his sons—even the youngest, Mioch, who was no more than a boy. Swiftly over the sea sailed the men of Lochlann, making no stop until they landed on the coast of Ulster.

When Cormac Mac Art heard of the great army from Lochlann which had invaded his kingdom, he sent messengers at once to the Hill of Allen, where Finn Mac Cool lived, bidding him come quickly with the Fianna, to protect Ireland from the enemy.

Finn gathered together the Fianna and set off for Ulster, meeting the army of Lochlann near the coast. They had a fierce battle there; and so many were the men of Lochlann, that at one time it seemed as though Finn and the Fianna could not fail to be defeated.

Oscar, Finn's young grandson, was so grieved to see his comrades fall that, in a despairing rage, he boldly rushed towards the standard of King Colga, cutting down all who stood in his way. Seeing him come, Colga met him, weapons ready, and the two of them fought mightily, the famed king of Lochlann and the red-haired youth; and for all Colga's skill and battle-wisdom, rash young Oscar's rage and courage prevailed, and he struck down Colga.

When the men of Lochlann saw their king lying dead, they became despondent; and though they fought on until evening, they had no heart in the fighting, and the Fianna had soon gained the advantage. At sunset the men of Lochlann fled from the battlefield, pursued by the Fianna. In the end, of that great army which had sailed so proudly

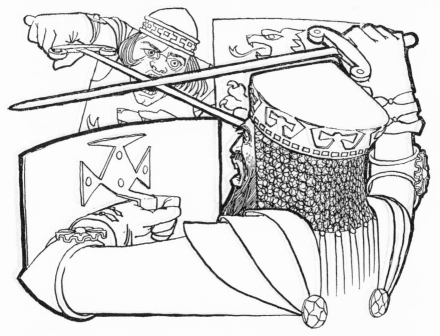

from Lochlann with its king, not one warrior, lord or prince was left alive, save Mioch, Colga's youngest son. And him alone, out of all the others, Finn spared, because he was no more than a boy; and when the fighting was done and the victors had rested, the Fianna marched southwards, taking Mioch with them.

Finn gave Mioch a home in his house on the flat-topped Hill of Allen, with servants and men of his own to wait on him; and he bade all the Fianna treat him with honour, as befitted the son of a king. But though Mioch grew up amongst the Fianna, hunted with them when they hunted, fought beside them when they fought, shared their life and their griefs and their pleasures, yet in his heart he ever hated them as the slayers of his father and his brothers, and he dreamt of revenge. He was always quiet and reserved and spoke little to his companions at any time, but he studied carefully the ways of the Fianna, their methods of fighting, the habits of each warrior, their favourite hunting-grounds and the places they frequented, against a day when he might find a use for this knowledge.

But even as Mioch watched the Fianna and bided his time, there was one amongst the Fianna who watched him: Conan the Bald. Conan the Bald was a great boaster and a glutton, lazy and spiteful and evil-tongued; yet when shamed into fighting, he could be fierce enough and a match for most men. Always looking about him for trouble, Conan had soon noticed Mioch's watchful silence and, in his turn, he spied on Mioch when he could.

One day when Finn and some of the leaders of the Fianna were talking together in council, debating on matters which they felt to need consideration, Conan stood up and said, 'In my opinion, lord, we waste our time arguing about trifles, and ignore the bigger matters. It seems to me that at this very moment the Fianna are in danger. You have in your house, Finn, one who has no cause to love you. One who knows too much about the men of the Fianna and their way of life, one who would not hesitate to use his knowledge to harm us all, had he the opportunity. Lord, you cannot have failed to see how, in the years he has dwelt among us, young Mioch has held himself aloof, cold and haughty and, I have no doubt—though he hides it well—resentful. To him, we are the men who killed his father and his brothers and so many of his people. He knows too much about us, and I fear that one day he will use his knowledge to our hurt.'

Finn thought this over for a while, and then he said, 'There may be wisdom in what you say, Conan. Certainly it is true that Mioch has no cause to love us. Yet what would you have me do?'

'Send him away, lord, to live by himself, where he can no longer watch us and learn our secrets, to use against us when he sees fit. If you will—since you are ever generous—give him land on which to build himself a house, since he is the son of a king. But send him away from Allen.'

And when Finn and the other leaders of the Fianna had discussed the matter further, they agreed with Conan the Bald and decided to do as he advised.

Finn sent for Mioch and said to him, 'In my house you have grown from a boy to a warrior, and the time has come when you need no more instruction in battlecraft, for you have learnt all that it is neces-sary for a prince and a warrior of the Fianna to know. You are the son of a king; it is fitting that you should have a home and a household of your own. Choose therefore, out of my lands, any two holdings that please you, and they shall be yours and your sons' for ever. And I will, moreover, give you cattle and goods, and help in the building of a house.'

Mioch heard Finn in silence; then when Finn had ceased, he said, quietly, coolly and unsmilingly, 'Your proposal is fair, lord, and pleases me. I would be well content with the land of Kenry, near the mouth of the River Shannon, and that land of many islands which lies opposite, on the other side of the river, by the mouth of the River Fergus.'

'They shall be yours,' said Finn; and he thought how Mioch had chosen well, for the lands were rich and fertile.

But to Mioch the richness of the lands was unimportant. He had chosen as he did because between the two stretches of land lay the broad River Shannon, with many little islands and hidden harbours, where a fleet of ships might lie at anchor unseen. And one day, he had sworn to himself, he would bring a fleet to Ireland, to avenge his father and his brothers and all the dead of Lochlann.

With Finn's help, Mioch built a house beside the river; and with goods and cattle bestowed on him by Finn, he settled in his new home; and for several years Finn and the Fianna saw no more of him and knew nothing of his manner of living. For none of them went to see him uninvited; and though he himself was still one of the Fianna, he had no dealings with them and never asked any single one of them to his home or offered them hospitality, but kept himself apart from all his former comrades.

And so things went for a few years, until one day when Finn and certain of the Fianna were hunting in Limerick. They intended the hunt to last several days and chose the top of the hill of Knockfierna as the place where they should set up their camp; and here they pitched their tents, collected heather and rushes for bedding, and built their cooking-place, a deep pit with a fire beside it. For the manner of their cooking was this: in the fire they would heat stones, and when these were hot, they would lay them in the bottom of the pit; upon these hot stones they would place their meat, then set more hot stones upon it, with a great pile of branches over the top of all, and in this rough oven they would leave the meat until it was cooked.

On this day, as the other men of the Fianna with their hounds drove the deer and the boar from cover on the plain, Finn and a few companions sat on the top of Knockfierna to rest themselves. Suddenly they looked up to see approaching them a tall warrior, clad as for battle in a coat of ring mail such as the men of Lochlann wore, with a many-coloured cloak over it and a gleaming helmet on his head. A long sword with a golden hilt hung at his side, and over his shoulder was slung his shield, while in his right hand he was carrying two sharp spears. He greeted Finn gravely and courteously, and Finn asked him, 'Who are you, stranger, and from where do you come?'

'The place from where I come is of no importance to us, lord. As for who I am: I am a poet.'

Finn, looking at him, laughed. 'I would say that the only poetry which you are likely to know, my friend, is the clash and clamour of battle; for seldom have I seen a warrior—let alone a poet—more warlike than you.'

'Nevertheless, lord, I am a poet, as I will prove to you, with your permission.'

'A hilltop is no place for reciting or for listening to poetry,' said Finn. 'Besides, we have come here to watch the chase below. Yet remain with us, my friend, until the hunting is done, and then you may come with us to the Hill of Allen to my house and entertain us with your poems. I can promise you a welcome and gifts to bear away with you.'

'I do not wish to go to your house, Finn; therefore I put you under bonds to hear my poem now, in this place, and to explain its meaning to me.'

Finn shrugged his shoulders. 'Well then, since you put me under bonds: recite your poem.'

The young stranger thereupon repeated a verse:

> By a river a house I saw,
> Famed through all years and evermore;
> Set with gems from roof to floor;
> The house of one skilled in age-old lore.
> No conqueror steps within its door;
> No thief can raid its treasure store.
> Not fire nor water can this house destroy;

And all who enter find feasting and joy.
Tell me the name of this house I saw,
With crystal roof and marble floor;
This house that stands on the river's shore.

When he had finished, Finn said, 'That is not hard; I can explain your poem easily. The house which you have described is Brugh of the Boyne, the palace of Angus of the Birds, the god of love. Being the home of a god, it cannot be burnt down or flooded by water or despoiled by robbers. And for all who enter it there is a welcome and feasting.'

'That is indeed the meaning of my poem,' said the stranger. 'Now here is another. Tell me the meaning of this, if you can,' and he recited:

In the east there lives a queen,
With a throne of crystal and a gown of green.
Small and shining, bright and gay,
Her countless children about her play.
Slowly, slowly she runs her course,
Yet she outstrips the swiftest horse.
What is the name of this glorious queen,
With her throne of crystal and her gown of green?

'That also is easy,' said Finn. 'The queen of whom you speak is the River Boyne. Her crystal couch is the clear sand on the bottom of the river, her green gown is the green plain through which she flows, her children are the fish in the water. And though the waters of the river flow slowly, yet in seven years they can cross the oceans of the whole world—and what horse could do that!'

'You have indeed given truly the meaning of both my poems,' said the young man.

'Seeing that I have answered your riddles, stranger, let you now answer my questions. Tell me, who are you and from where have you come?'

But before the young man could answer, Conan the Bald, who had been watching him carefully and frowningly while he spoke his poems, broke in, 'You may be the wisest of all men, Finn, but today you have not the wisdom to know a foe from a friend. This is Mioch, son of Colga, as you would know had he not chosen to keep himself hidden from us, never coming to Allen to see how we did, nor inviting any of us to a feasting, for all he is yet one of the Fianna.'

'Is that my fault?' asked Mioch. 'If neither Finn nor any man of the Fianna has feasted with me in my house, it is not for want of feasts there—for my house is never without a feast worthy of any king. It is because no man of the Fianna has seen fit to come to my home to ask how I fared. And if you say that you were not invited; then to that I can answer that since I, too, am one of the Fianna, and since I was brought up in Finn's household, there need be no formality between us. But let that now be in the past; for today I have a feast prepared for you, and I put you all under bonds not to refuse it. I have two houses and in each there is a feast. One is the House of the Island on the farther side of the river, and the other is the House of the Rowan Trees, which stands only a little way off from this hill. It is to the House of the Rowan Trees that I would have you come.'

To this Finn agreed; and, because they were under bonds, Conan the Bald agreed also, though unwillingly.

'Then I will leave you, lord, and go on ahead to see that all is made ready,' said Mioch; and having pointed out to them the way that they should go, he left them.

When he had gone, Finn arranged that his son Oisin and five other warriors of the Fianna, together with their followers, should remain on the hill until the rest of the hunting-party came to join them, by which time Finn would have sent a messenger back to them, telling them what manner of welcome he had found at Mioch's house; and then, if they heard that all was well with him, they were to go after him to the House of the Rowan Trees. This having been settled between them, Finn set off with those others whom Mioch had invited, amongst them Conan the Bald and Gaul Mac Morna; while with Oisin were left Dermot O'Dyna, Finn's nephew, Keelta Mac Ronan, the swiftest runner among the Fianna, Fiachna—Little Raven—who was a son of Finn, and Innsa, Finn's foster-son.

Following the direction pointed out to them by Mioch, Finn and the others soon came to a green plain overlooking the river, near by the only ford, upon which stood a fine, large house, surrounded by a grove of rowan trees with their scarlet berries.

'A handsome house indeed,' they said amongst themselves, and wondered greatly that they had never seen it before, though they had passed in sight of that place often enough; for it was not the house which Finn had built for Mioch.

But as they approached the house through the rowan trees, they saw how it seemed deserted, with never a soul in sight, neither their host nor any of his servants.

'I do not like the look of this,' said Finn. But because of the bonds that were on him, he did not turn back.

The wide doors of the house were open, and though Finn might hesitate to enter, not so Conan the Bald, who was, for all his suspicions of Mioch, beginning to think with pleasure of a meal. Conan walked boldly through the nearest door and into the hall and took a good look around. After a few moments he came out again to the others, grinning broadly.

'I have never seen a finer house, lord,' he said. 'Indeed, I warrant that nowhere in Ireland is there a finer house than this. And if the food is worthy of the house—then I, for one, am ready for it.' He turned round and went back into the house, and Finn and all the others followed him.

Inside, the hall was as splendid as Conan had declared it to be. The wooden walls, in which were seven doors, were clean and polished like ivory, and painted in every gay colour. In the middle of the hall burnt a bright fire with darting flames and not a trace of smoke, giving out a sweet, refreshing scent. Around the fire were set couches covered with soft furs and costly rugs; and though there was still no sign of any servants, such surroundings seemed to promise rich fare and plenty to drink, so Finn and the others sat down and waited.

After a little time, Mioch came into the hall. He said nothing, but stood looking at Finn and the men of the Fianna one after the other; then, still without speaking, he left the hall by the same door through which he had come, closing it behind him as he went.

Finn and the rest were surprised at this, but they made no comment, and only waited for him to return. However, Mioch did not come back, and at last Finn said, 'This is strange behaviour in a host, that he leaves his guests alone and unattended. Had we not seen Mioch here just now, I would think that perhaps his servants had prepared the feast in his other house by mistake. Yet Mioch was here and said nothing of this. Truly, it is most strange.'

'There is something stranger than that,' said Gaul Mac Morna. 'Look at the fire, Finn. When we entered here, it was burning brightly, without any smoke, and gave out a sweet scent. But now, see how it smokes with a black smoke, and how foully it smells.'

'I see something stranger than that,' said Glas Mac Encarda. 'Look at the walls of the house. When we came in they were clean and polished and painted in bright colours. Now, see, they are no more than rough planks hacked with a blunt axe and fastened together with withies.'

'I see something stranger than that,' said Foilan, son of Aed the Lesser, in a low voice. 'When we entered here, the hall had seven doors, all wide open to let in the sunshine. And now, look, there is only one small, narrow doorway, fastened close.'

'And I see something even stranger than that,' said Conan the Bald. 'When we came in here we sat down on soft couches spread with rugs and furs. Where have those couches and rugs and furs gone to? Because we are now sitting on the floor—and as cold as the first snow of the winter it feels!'

Finn looked around him and saw that it was as they said. 'My friends,' he said firmly, 'you know that I never stay in a house that has only one door. Let one of you break it open, so that we can go once more into the clean air and the sunlight, out of this filthy, smoky hovel.'

'The more quickly that is done, the better,' said Conan, and he made to jump up and go to the door. But he found that he could in no way do so. He gave a cry of distress. 'Alas! Here is a thing that is the strangest of all. I am fixed by some enchantment to the floor of this place and I cannot get up.'

Upon this all the others tried to rise, and found that they, too, could not move from the floor; and for a while they could only look at one another in dismay as they realized their plight.

Then Gaul Mac Morna spoke. 'This is some evil planned by Mioch against us. If we are to fight it or to escape from it, we should know what it is that threatens us. You have the gift of wisdom and understanding, lord. Put your thumb beneath your tooth of knowledge and tell us the nature of our danger.'

Finn put his thumb under his tooth of knowledge and was silent for a while. Then he took his thumb from his mouth and gave a groan.

'May the gods grant that you groan only because you chanced to bite your thumb,' said Gaul.

'Alas,' said Finn, 'I did not. It is the truth at which I groan. We have been caught in a trap by Mioch, and long has he been waiting for this day. My knowledge tells me that there is, at this very moment, in his House of the Island, a great army from over the sea. In Mioch's house are King Sinsar of the Battles, who calls himself the King of the World, and his son Borba and many warriors of note, and the three tall sorcerer kings from the Island of the Torrent, who are like ravening dragons and have never yet yielded to an enemy. It is they, the three sorcerers, who have built for Mioch this house of enchantments to be our death. For here, on the cold floor of this house, must we sit until they come to slay us, and we shall be unable to strike a single blow to save ourselves, for my knowledge tells me that the spell which binds us here cannot be broken until the blood of these three kings is sprinkled on the floor. Only then shall we be able to move and rise again.'

They all heard him with horror and began to lament their fate; while some of them wept that they should have to die like cattle, instead of fighting bravely, sword in hand. But Finn said, 'Tears and sighs will not help us, my friends. Therefore let us wait for death as calmly as we may. For we are, after all, the men of the Fianna. Come, let us sound once more our battle-cry, the Dord-Fiann, and take comfort from it, before it is too late.'

So all together, sitting on the cold floor of the enchanted house which had been prepared for their doom, they sounded their battle-cry in unison, slowly and sadly.

Meanwhile, Oisin waited on the hill of Knockfierna with the other warriors of the Fianna. The day wore on and night drew closer, and still there was no word from Finn of the welcome that had been offered him at Mioch's house. Oisin stared into the distance, frowning. 'I do not like this silence of my father's,' he said at last. 'I fear that some ill has befallen him in the House of the Rowan Trees. Someone must go there and bring us back word of him.'

Oisin's half-brother, Finn's young son Fiachna, immediately said, 'I will go, Oisin.' And in the same instant a bold youth named Innsa, who was Finn's foster-son, leapt to his feet and offered to go with Fiachna.

They set off together at once and walked quickly in the direction which Finn and his friends had taken, and before long they came in sight of the river and the ford and the narrow path leading up from the ford; and close by there, the grove of rowan trees. As they approached the house through the dusk, they could hear from within the sound of Finn and his comrades chanting, loudly and clearly, their war-cry.

'All must be well with Finn and the others, that they chant the Dord-Fiann while they feast,' exclaimed Innsa, much relieved.

But Fiachna went closer, to the very walls of the house, and said uncertainly, 'They chant the Dord-Fiann, yes. But how sadly and slowly. I fear that all is not well with them, Innsa.'

'Surely,' said Innsa, 'if they were in danger we should hear the clash of arms. They would not be chanting so calmly.'

Fiachna shook his head in the dim light. 'I like it not.'

While they were talking thus outside the house, inside, Finn caught the sound of voices and bade his companions be silent. Then he called out, 'Is that you, Fiachna?'

'It is I, lord.'

'Then come no nearer, my son, for this place abounds in spells. This house is a trap set by Mioch, and we are in the power of the three sorcerer kings of the Island of the Torrent.' And he told Fiachna of all that he had learnt when he put his thumb under his tooth of knowledge, even to the fact that nothing could break the spell which bound him and his companions save the blood of the three kings.

'This is indeed a disaster,' said Fiachna, appalled.

'Who is it with you, my son?' asked Finn. 'For I heard you speaking before I called to you.'

'It is I, lord, your foster-son Innsa.'

'Alas!' exclaimed Finn. 'A youth whom it is my duty to protect, not to lead into danger! Fiachna, my son, leave this accursed place at once and save my foster-child, for soon our enemies will be coming here to kill us, and I would not have Innsa slain.'

'You have been the kindest of foster-fathers to me,' said Innsa. 'What a poor return for your kindness it would be if I left you now.'

'And I, too, am staying, my father, no matter who comes,' declared Fiachna.

'You are two good sons,' said Finn, 'and I fear that only danger and hardship lie before you. Yet if you are determined to stay and fight, there can be no better place for you to meet the enemy than at the ford. To reach us, Mioch and his friends must cross the river from the House of the Island. There is but the one ford, and I saw that the path which leads up from it to the rowan grove is steep and narrow. Two warriors alone, standing at the entrance to this path, could, for a time, hold the way to the rowan grove against an army. And who knows, soon Oisin and our friends may grow anxious and come after you, and so save us all.'

Fiachna and Innsa went down to the ford and looked carefully at it in the twilight. 'One man could defend this place as well as two,' said Fiachna. 'Do you stay here, Innsa, while I go over the river to the House of the Island and see how many are gathered against us and whether, should Oisin and the others come, we might attack the house while they are unprepared. If on the way I meet with any of the foreign warriors, I can try to mislead them in the darkness.' He set off, leaving Innsa by the ford.

But the darkness, which he trusted to conceal him, hid also a small band of warriors who were approaching the ford quietly; these men Fiachna passed at a distance and did not see. They were led by a chieftain of King Sinsar, who had left the feasting in the House of the Island, hoping to please his king by slaying Finn and bringing his head to him.

This chieftain and his men came stealthily to the ford, and looking across the river, the chieftain thought that he saw a man standing on the opposite bank, and he called out, 'Who are you, that stand by the ford on the other side of the river?'

'My name is Innsa, and I am of the household of Finn Mac Cool.'

'Then you are well met,' shouted the chieftain, 'for we are going to the House of the Rowan Trees to fetch Finn's head for the King of the World, and you can show us the way, since we are strangers here.'

'That would be a curious thing for me to do, seeing that it is Finn himself who has sent me to guard the ford for him,' said Innsa. 'I warn you, you will find it hard to cross to my side of the river while I am here.'

The chieftain laughed and said to his followers, 'The young man boasts loudly enough. Cross the river and see if his deeds match his proud words.'

They all did as they were bidden and ran, splashing, across the river at the ford; but because the path up the river's bank on the other side was so narrow, only one or two at a time could attack Innsa. And he, besides, had the advantage of higher ground, and he struck out at them mightily and tumbled them into the river, one after another. When he realized that so many of his men were being slain, the foreign chieftain grew angry, and taking up his sword and his shield, he crossed the river after them and fell upon Innsa himself. By this time Innsa had been fighting hard for many minutes and he was wounded and weary, so that, for all his advantage of position, he was finally worsted by the more experienced chieftain, who struck him down and cut off his head. Then, deciding he had too few warriors left to attempt an attack on Finn, he crossed back again to the other side of the river and, together with his remaining men, returned in the direction of the House of the Island, bearing Innsa's head with him.

On the way he met Fiachna coming back towards the ford after having learnt as much as he could about the enemy. Meeting Fiachna so close to the House of the Island, the chieftain thought he was one of Mioch's men and spoke to him.

Fiachna, suddenly afraid that, in his absence, the enemy had tried to cross the ford, asked him from where he had come.

'From the ford across the river,' replied the chieftain. 'We thought to go to the House of the Rowan Trees and slay Finn Mac Cool, but at the ford there was a brave young warrior who slew many of my men. However, in the end I killed him, and now I am bringing his head as a trophy to my king, because he was indeed a mighty warrior, though young.' And he held up Innsa's head for Fiachna to see.

Fiachna peered through the twilight and then took the head in his hands and kissed the cold cheeks. 'My little foster-brother, how short a time ago these eyes were bright and this mouth was laughing and talking with me!' Then in sudden rage he turned to the chieftain and said, 'Do you know to whom you have given this youth's head?'

The chieftain was startled. 'You come from the House of the Island; do you not serve Mioch, or my own master, the King of the World?'

'I do not. And nor, in another minute, shall you.' And with that Fiachna drew his sword and fell upon the chieftain. In a few moments the fight was over, the chieftain lay dead and his men were fled. Fiachna cut off his head, and carrying it and the head of Innsa, he returned to the ford and crossed the river. On the opposite bank he found Innsa's body, and sorrowfully he buried it with his head under the green grass. Then taking up the chieftain's head, he went to the House of the Rowan Trees and called out to Finn.

'My son,' cried Finn anxiously, 'we have heard fighting at the ford, then silence. Tell us, how did it go?'

'Your foster-son Innsa held the ford against a number of the enemy, whose bodies now lie in the river.'

'And Innsa, how is it with him?'

'He died at the hands of a foreign chieftain, my father.'

'Did you, my son, stand by and see him slain?'

'I was not there, my father. Had I been, he would not have died—or we would have died together. Yet I have avenged his death and I bring you the head of the man who slew him. And Innsa himself I buried where he fell, as you would have wished me to do.'

Finn wept; and then he said, 'Truly, no man ever had better or braver sons than I. But go back now, Fiachna, and guard the ford, and may our friends come in time to save us.'

Fiachna went down again to the river and sat on a rock above the ford in the darkness and waited.

He did not have long to wait. When the foreign chieftain did not return to the House of the Island, his brother Kironn grew anxious. 'Let us go and seek him,' he said to his own men.

At the ford they saw the dead men lying in the water and they saw, also, Fiachna on the other side. Kironn called out to him, asking him his name, and who it was that had slain so many of his brother's men.

'I am Fiachna, son of Finn Mac Cool, and he has sent me to guard this ford for him. As for your other question: it angers me too much for me to answer it in words. Come over the river, and I will give you an answer in deeds.'

Kironn forthwith led his men over the river; but as they could only attack Fiachna two at a time, Fiachna slew them all save one; and that one man fled back to the House of the Island with word of what had befallen his companions and his lord.

When Mioch heard what had happened, he was angry. 'These men were fools to go without my guidance. They are strangers here, and moreover, they do not know the skill and courage of the Fianna as I do. Besides, Finn is my enemy; it is for me to kill him and avenge my father and my brothers.'

He chose out a large band of the bravest of his men and made ready to go to the House of the Rowan Trees. 'Bring us food and drink of the best to take with us,' he called to his servants as he was arming himself. 'For amongst those at the House of the Rowan Trees is Conan the Bald—a greedy guzzler if ever there was one—and I have a score to settle with him, for it was he who first urged Finn to banish me to this place. It will be rare sport to torment Conan before he dies, with the sight and smell of food which lies just beyond his reach.'

And so, carrying meat and drink in a basket, they set out for the ford. Fiachna heard them when they reached the farther side of the river. Weary and wounded, he stood up and waited for them to cross.

Mioch saw him through the darkness, but did not know who he was. 'Which of my old comrades of the Fianna is it, there on the other bank of the river?' he called out.

'It is I, Fiachna.'

Mioch feigned pleasure. 'I am glad indeed of it. For in the years I spent in Finn's house, you, Fiachna, were ever kind and a good friend to me, and there was never ill will between us.'

'What a liar you are, Mioch,' said Fiachna drily. 'There was never ill will between us: but there was no friendship either. Of all the men of the Fianna, I think that I had the least of all to do with you. But I remember well how kind my father Finn was to you always. Small gratitude have you shown for that!'

This angered Mioch, who said, 'You had best go from the ford, Fiachna, and let us cross over, or you will find that you have not long to live.'

'I am staying here, Mioch. You will find me when you cross over. I only regret that you did not come earlier, before I was wounded, for then I should have been able to give you a warmer welcome.'

At that Mioch sent his warriors over the river; but Fiachna, weary and wounded as he was, overcame them all, until only Mioch was left; and then furiously, stepping over the bodies of his men, Mioch fell upon Fiachna in the narrow path, and they fought long and savagely.

Meanwhile, on the hill of Knockfierna, when Fiachna and Innsa did not return, Oisin became more anxious. 'Things must be ill indeed with Finn, that neither Fiachna nor Innsa has returned with tidings of him.'

'Maybe they have found the feast so pleasing that they have joined in and are in no hurry to leave it, to tell us that all is well,' someone suggested.

But Oisin was not convinced; and Dermot O'Dyna, Finn's nephew, said, 'I am going to see for myself, Oisin. For, like you, I believe that something is amiss.' He looked about him at his friends in the firelight. 'Who will come with me?'

A young warrior named Fatha stepped forward. 'I will, Dermot.'

They ran off together through the darkness; and while they were still at a distance from the river, they heard the clashing of weapons, and they hurried on. Then they heard a cry, brave but weak, and Dermot said, 'That is Fiachna's battle-cry. He must be fighting alone against an enemy.'

They went even faster, until they came close enough to the ford to see, in the light of the now-risen moon, how Fiachna, hardly able to stand for his wounds, still held off Mioch's attack, though he was too weak to do more than defend himself from the strokes of the other's sword.

Dermot halted in his headlong run and stood undecided. 'We cannot reach them in time to save Fiachna; and if I throw my spear, Fatha, I may strike Fiachna instead of Mioch.'

'Have no fear, Dermot,' said Fatha. 'You have never yet missed a mark with your spear.'

Encouraged, Dermot flung his spear and struck Mioch full in the body. Then he ran down the slope towards him, shouting to him to spare Fiachna.

Mioch, with Dermot's spear through him, gasped, 'If you wished me to spare Finn's son, you should have spared me, Dermot.' With his last strength he raised his sword and brought it down upon Fiachna's head, and both of them fell to the ground in the same instant, just as Dermot and Fatha reached them.

'Wait here and guard the ford, Fatha, while I go on to find Finn,' said Dermot. And stopping only to free his spear and to cut off Mioch's head for Finn, he hurried on to the House of the Rowan Trees and beat loudly on the door with the butt of his spear, calling to Finn and the others.

Finn instantly cried out, 'Do not attempt to come in here, Dermot, for there is an evil spell on the place. But tell me—for we have heard fighting at the ford—how fares my son Fiachna?'

'Your brave son fought single-handed against many men.'

'And then, what?'

'The Little Raven is dead, Finn. He was slain by Mioch. But I have brought you Mioch's head.'

For many moments there was silence while Finn mourned his son. Then with a sigh he set aside his grief for the dead to take thought for the living and their plight. 'Often in the past have you helped the Fianna when they were sorely pressed, Dermot,' he said. 'May it be so again today. Yet this adventure is perhaps the worst of all that the Fianna have faced, for it is hard to fight against enchantment. Only by the blood of the three sorcerer kings of the Island of the Torrent can we be freed from the spell which binds us here. Go to the ford, Dermot, and guard it against the foreigners. If you can but hold off the enemy until sunrise, then all may be well. For at dawn, if they have heard no word from us, surely Oisin and all the Fianna will come.'

'Fatha and I will keep the ford, never fear, lord,' said Dermot. And he would have gone back at once to the ford, but Conan the Bald groaned and called out, 'Oh, it was an ill moment when I entered this place, and an ill moment when I sat down, not to rise again. But the worst pain of all is to have been so long without food or drink. There will be meat and ale in plenty in the House of the Island—I would I were filling my belly with it. Oh, Dermot, I can bear my hunger no longer. Go and fetch me food and drink.'

'Our lord Finn sits here held by a spell and any moment likely to be slain; Fiachna and Innsa are dead; there are but two of us, Fatha and I, to hold a great army off; and you, Conan, are asking me to risk my life to get you food. Surely there was never such a glutton in all the world.'

'Handsome Dermot, beloved of all women,' sneered Conan, 'if I were a pretty young girl, you would take any risk to do me a little favour. But I am only poor Conan, your old companion in the Fianna, whom you have always hated and despised; so out of spite you will let me stay here without food and drink—and I have no doubt you hope that I may die before the spell is broken!'

'Hold your tongue, Conan!' shouted Dermot. 'I will go and fetch you food and drink. Truly, it is better to risk my life than to have you reviling me for the rest of your days.'

He went back to the river's bank to Fatha, and said, 'I must leave you to guard the ford alone, for Conan is demanding food and drink of me, and I must go to the House of the Island to fetch them.'

'There is food and drink in a basket down by the water,' said Fatha, pointing. 'I can see it plainly in the moonlight. For some reason which we now shall never know, Mioch and his men brought food with them when they came across the ford. Go and fetch the basket and take it to Conan.'

'No,' said Dermot. 'If I were to do that, he would never cease to blame me for giving him food which I had taken from dead men who were not able to prevent me from doing as I would. I have no wish to be the butt of Conan's malice for the rest of my life. I shall go to the House of the Island.'

So Dermot made his way to the House of the Island; and as he approached he could hear the sounds of feasting and revelry from within; for as yet, none of the guests knew that their host was dead. Dermot looked through a doorway and saw King Sinsar of the Battles and his son Borba and the three sorcerer kings of the Island of the Torrent sitting at the high table, and all about them their lords and warriors and many of Mioch's men. Everyone was laughing and eating and drinking, and servants went about filling the drinking-horns and carving meat. Dermot slipped through the doorway and stood just inside, a little way along the wall, where it was dark and the torchlight did not reach. He drew his sword and waited. After a while one of the servants passed by him, bearing a drinking-horn filled with wine. Swiftly Dermot struck off his head and caught the drinking-horn as it fell, so skilfully that not a drop of wine was spilt. Then, fearing that it might be only too soon that the man's body was discovered, he set down the horn carefully by the door and walked boldly into the lighted hall and took a full platter off a table. Then with both drinking-horn and platter he went out from the house and back to the ford.

At the ford he found Fatha asleep, wrapped in his cloak among all the dead; and he went on past him up to the House of the Rowan Trees. At the door he called out to Conan, 'I have brought you your food and your drink, but how shall I get it to you?'

Conan, never at a loss when food was in question, said quickly, 'There is a gap in the wall, a little to one side of the door, I can see the moonlight through it. Throw me the food through there.'

So, piece by piece, Dermot threw the meat through the crack in the wall, and Conan caught each piece as it came and stuffed it into his mouth. When all was gone, Dermot said, 'I have brought you a large horn of wine, but how are you going to drink it?'

'You are light on your feet and good at jumping, Dermot. As we came here, I saw that there is a rock which stands behind the house. Climb up on that rock and jump over the house and make a hole in the roof. Then jump over the house again, and pour the wine through the hole.'

Dermot climbed up the rock and leapt over the house, making a hole in the roof with his spear. Then he climbed up the rock again, carrying the drinking-horn. Lightly he leapt over the house once more and poured the wine through the hole in the roof. Through the hole went the wine, right into Conan's greedy mouth.

Then Dermot returned to the ford and found Fatha still asleep. He did not wake him, but sat down beside him and waited, wondering which would come first: dawn and the Fianna, or the enemy.

As the night grew older and Mioch did not return to the House of the Island, someone was sent to the river to see if all was well with him and his men; and finding only dead bodies about the ford and in the water, he returned with word of this.

The three sorcerer kings of the Island of the Torrent were loud in deploring Mioch's rashness. 'He was unwise to have gone without us to aid him,' they said. 'And besides, it is through our spells that Finn Mac Cool is held in the House of the Rowan Trees, therefore to us belongs the right to kill him.' And calling up a great body of their men, they armed themselves and set off for the ford. Once there, they called across the river to Dermot, whom they could see as a shadow in the moonlight, 'Who are you, waiting there at the ford?'

'I am Dermot O'Dyna, and I am Finn Mac Cool's warrior. He has ordered me to guard this ford for him, so beware how you cross the river.'

When they heard his name, they sought to win him to their side with flattery and pleasant words, for his fame, like Finn's, had reached even to their land; but Dermot only answered, 'You are wasting your time. So long as I am alive I shall hold this ford, for Finn has bidden it.' And with that he stood up, his weapons ready, and frowned at them across the water.

At once a number of warriors came over the river to attack him, yet he met their charge calmly, not even troubling to arouse Fatha from his sleep. But the clash of arms and the shouts of the attackers awoke Fatha and he leapt to his feet and looked about him, startled. Then, seeing that Dermot was fighting alone, he was angry. 'That was ill done, Dermot, to keep a battle to yourself and not share it with me.' And in his anger he ran at Dermot and would have struck him.

But Dermot cried out, 'I have enough toil to defend myself from our enemies; must I defend myself from you as well, Fatha? Save your anger for these foreign warriors: our quarrel can keep until another time.'

So Fatha, recovering himself, stood beside Dermot and together they cast down a score or more of the enemy.

Seeing their men so easily overcome, the three sorcerer kings themselves crossed the ford and joined in the attack; but before they had time to call up spells and enchantments to overcome Dermot and Fatha, the three kings were slain; and their remaining men fled back to the House of the Island.

Then, remembering what Finn had told him, Dermot triumphantly cut off the heads of the three kings and hastened with them to the House of the Rowan Trees, calling out as he approached, 'Lord, Fatha and I have slain the three kings of the Island of the Torrent. Here we bring you their heads.'

Joyfully Finn answered him, 'Sprinkle the door with their blood, Dermot.'

Dermot did so, and the door opened with a loud noise and he and Fatha went into the house. Swinging the heads by their hair, they sprinkled the blood of the three kings all about the floor; and immediately Finn and his companions found that they could rise. Delightedly they embraced one another and crowded about Dermot and Fatha, rejoicing at their deliverance, until Finn said warningly, 'All danger is not yet passed. We still have King Sinsar of the Battles—he who calls himself the King of the World—and his son to reckon with. When they hear how the three sorcerer kings have died, they will not sail tamely away to their own country, but will hurry here to avenge their allies. I am still weak from the enchantment—and my good friends likewise, I have no doubt—and so shall we remain until the dawn, when the sun will rise and dispel the last traces of sorcery. Therefore go back to the ford, good Dermot and Fatha, and we shall join you with our weapons as soon as we are able.'

The two warriors returned to the river and waited. They did not have long to wait; for as soon as the survivors of the fighting reached the House of the Island and told their tale, Borba, the son of King Sinsar—who, of those gathered there for Mioch's sake, was the greatest warrior of all, save King Sinsar himself—spoke out and said scornfully, 'Poor warriors indeed they must all have been who fell at the ford to no more than two of Finn's men. Let them beware, these two men of the Fianna, for I, Borba, am going to avenge my friends and fetch the head of Finn Mac Cool to lay at my father's feet.'

And with that he set off with half of his father's army, intent on proving his prowess. To Dermot and Fatha, waiting in the moonlight, the great body of men approaching them seemed like a vast sea, and they feared that they might be swept away before its onslaught, leaving Finn and his companions to their fate.

'We must spare ourselves from now on, Fatha,' said Dermot. 'It matters little how few we kill, so long as we can hold them off from the House of the Rowan Trees until the dawn. Let us save our strength for as long as we may.'

This time the foreigners did not stop to call across the river to their adversaries, they crossed the ford at once and swarmed up the bank on the opposite side like a dark tide. Yet at first they gained no advantage from their numbers, because of the narrow way up the slope; and

Dermot and Fatha, fighting resolutely, held them off while the sky lightened in the east.

They were both fighting with such determination that they did not even notice when the first rays of the sun glinted on the armour of their enemies; and they knew it was dawn only when they heard the welcome sound of the voices of Finn and his companions—now freed entirely from the spell—as they raced down the slope behind them to join in the battle.

Wildly raged the fighting in the narrow pathway, until many of the enemy were driven back into the river, followed by the Fianna. And it was in the middle of the ford that Borba met Gaul Mac Morna. Well did Gaul live up to his name—Gaul of the Blows—for with one mighty stroke of his sword he cut off Borba's head, so that it fell into the water.

The enemy was dismayed, but still fought bravely on, and a messenger hastened to the House of the Island to King Sinsar, with word of the death of his son.

Sinsar immediately arose; and though in his heart he sorrowed for the loss of his son, there was no sorrow in his voice, only anger and the cold desire for vengeance, as he bade all those of his men who had remained with him make ready to follow him to the ford.

When Finn and Dermot and the others saw the rest of Sinsar's vast army approaching with their banners flying and their arms gleaming in the sun, they knew that, for all their courage and their battle skill, they were doomed. A mere handful of men, they could not fight for ever against so great an enemy. Then, even as they watched their foes massing on the farther bank of the river—countless, well-armed, determined warriors led by a king who was famed for his battlecraft and the number of his conquests—they heard behind them a familiar war-cry, sounding in well-loved voices; and they looked up to see behind them, at the top of the slope, Oisin and all the Fianna, come from the hill of Knockfierna to find them. They raised a cheer, all their doubts forgotten.

Soon the battle was raging on both sides of the river and all across the ford. Wherever the fighting was thickest, there was Finn, calling out in his great voice above the din and clash of arms, encouraging and praising, and increasing the strength and valour of the Fianna by his presence.

Finn's red-haired grandson, Oscar, resting for a moment from the fighting, looked about him and saw, not far off, the standard of King Sinsar and the great king himself, guarded by picked warriors. And he saw, too, how, wherever that standard went, the Fianna were swept back from its path. This sight angered him, and in his customary impetuous fashion, caring nothing for the risk, gripping his sword in his hands, he ran forward, right through the ranks of Sinsar's guard, towards the standard and the king, with such violence that no one could prevent him.

Sinsar saw him coming and marvelled at the young warrior's rash courage. Then, noticing his red hair gleaming in the sunshine as it hung below his helmet, and seeing his youth and his famed beauty, he knew him for Finn's grandson and he laughed aloud in his joy and gestured his men aside. 'This combat is mine,' he said. 'For this is surely Oscar, son of Oisin, the grandson of Finn Mac Cool. Finn, I have heard, loves him above all other men. Now shall you see me avenge my son Borba by taking from Finn what he most dreads to lose.'

Sinsar met Oscar's attack with violence, while all those near enough to watch looked on as they fought. At first the king had supposed, from his youth, that Oscar would prove a poor warrior; but when he found how mistaken he was, he grew angry and doubled his efforts against him. For a while Oscar was driven back, unable to do more than defend himself. Then, in a sudden spurt of rage, he attacked in his turn, so unexpectedly and with such a mighty blow of his sword, that he cut the king's head from his body.

At once a great cry of triumph rose up from the Fianna, and the enemy fled in confusion; those who were not slain as they fled making wildly for their ships, beached near the House of the Island, in the hope that they might escape to see their own land again. Finn and the Fianna had won yet another glorious battle.

★   ★   ★

The geis, or 'bond', by which Mioch lays it upon Finn, first to listen to his poems and then to come to his house, is a frequent circumstance of Celtic legend. It could not be disregarded by the person upon whom it was laid. In the story of Kilhwch and Olwen we have seen how Kilhwch's stepmother puts him under bonds to marry Olwen or no one.

Riddling verses, such as those which Mioch propounds to Finn, were very popular amongst the ancient Irish. A respected warrior and chieftain was expected to be able to guess the answers. Mioch's second riddle, likening the River Boyne to a fair queen, may put us in mind of Boann, goddess and first cause of the Boyne.

7

OISIN, SON OF FINN MAC COOL

No warrior was allowed to join the Fianna unless he had first passed certain severe tests. He had to be able to leap over a rod held up at the height of his brow, and to run at full speed beneath a rod held as low as his knee, and while running he had to be able to pluck out a thorn from his foot without slackening his speed. As proof of his fighting skill, he was buried to his waist in the ground and, holding his shield and armed only with a hazel stick, he had then to defend himself successfully against the attack of nine warriors casting their spears at him. As a further trial of his ability, his hair was carefully braided into plaits and he was chased through a wood by the Fianna; if he reached the other side of the wood without being overtaken and without snapping a single dry stick beneath his feet, and if his hair were not in any way disarranged at the end of the chase, he was accepted amongst them.

As well as these feats of skill and strength, a warrior of the Fianna was supposed to be able to recite the old poems and, if need be, to compose new verses of his own, observing the accepted styles of Gaelic poesy; and to live according to certain rules of conduct laid down by Finn. Here are a few of Finn's maxims which might still be applicable today:

Do not beat your dog without just cause; and do not accuse your wife unless you are certain she is at fault.

Let two-thirds of your gentleness be shown to women and children and to poets; and show no violence to the common folk.

Do not boast or be stubborn without good cause; it is shameful to brag of what you cannot perform.

So long as you live, do not forsake your lord; and neither for gold nor for any other reward desert a man whom you have promised to protect.

Bear no tales and tell no lies; do not talk too much or be too ready to judge others.

Do not stir up strife against yourself, however good a man you are.

Do not drink too much in taverns; and do not complain of the old.

Give freely of food; and take no miserly man as your friend.

Be more ready to give than to refuse; and follow after gentleness.

And it was Gaul Mac Morna, in prowess second only to Finn, who said: A man lives after his life, but not after his honour.

When Finn Mac Cool was young, not long after he had freed the stronghold of Tara from the peril of the Monster of the Flaming Breath and had been given the leadership of the Fianna by the High King of Ireland, he was returning one evening with his followers to his house on the Hill of Allen after a day's hunting. A mile or so from home, a red hind sprang up from the undergrowth and fled before them. The hounds immediately gave chase and pursued the deer towards the stronghold of Allen. But she ran so fast that she outstripped all the hounds and horses that followed her save only Finn's two favourite hounds, Bran and Skolaun. Bran and Skolaun were more than ordinary hounds, swifter than any others and gifted with human understanding, for they were the children of the sister of Finn's mother, who had been changed into a hound bitch by the enchantments of a rival who loved her husband, and in that shape had given birth to them.

When Finn, riding ahead of his companions, came up with the two hounds and the hind, they were close to the gates of the stronghold, and to Finn's amazement, the hind was lying down at her ease, resting from the chase, while Bran and Skolaun frisked around her, every won and then nuzzling her and licking her head, while she seemed unafraid.

Finn knew at once that there was some enchantment about the hind, and he bade the Fianna leash the other hounds and do her no harm. And when Finn entered his house, she followed him in, along with Bran and Skolaun.

That night Finn awoke from his sleep suddenly and saw standing beside his bed the fairest young woman he had ever seen.

'I am Sav,' she said to him. 'Bov the Red, the king of the gods, is my father. I was that hind which was chased by your hounds, but only Bran and Skolaun knew me for what I really was. I am loved by one of the immortals, but because I cannot return his love, he put on me the shape of a deer, and in that shape I have been for three years. Yet I learnt from one who pitied me that could I but win the protection of Finn Mac Cool, my own shape would be restored to me and I should be safe from all enchantments, so long as I stayed within the stronghold of Allen.'

Finn looked at her with delight and astonishment. 'Lady,' he said, 'my home is yours, for as long as you care to remain in it.'

So Sav remained at Allen, and Finn took her as his wife; and never were two people happier or more in love than they. For almost a year Finn never left her side. He took no more joy in hunting or in feats of arms, but passed day after day at home in her company.

But there comes an ending to all things, and there was an evening when messengers came to Finn from the High King at Tara, with news that the ships of the men of Lochlann had been sighted off the coast, and the Fianna were needed to defend Ireland.

'It will not be for long that we shall be parted,' said Finn to Sav. 'The thought that you wait here for me will give added strength to my hands. The men of Lochlann will be driven from the shores of Ireland more quickly than ever before, and then I shall be with you once again. But, while I am absent, beware of the enchantments of the immortals.'

Finn and his men marched away to Tara, and together with the other warriors of Ireland, they attacked the men of Lochlann as they landed from their long ships. Meanwhile, in Allen, every day Sav would sit on the ramparts, watching for Finn's return.

One morning she saw a tall man with two hounds at his heels hastening up the hillside. The sunlight shone on his fair hair, and as he raised his eyes to the ramparts above him, Sav leapt to her feet, crying out in gladness, 'It is Finn come home, and Bran and Skolaun with him!' and she ran to the gate and out of the gate down the Hill of Allen, calling joyfully to him.

He stood and waited for her, smiling with the lips of Finn; and the two hounds stood by him with lolling tongues. Her arms flung wide, Sav came to him, laughing and eager. But when she was close, she knew that though he had Finn's shape, he was not Finn; and that though the two hounds beside him had the shapes of Bran and Skolaun, they were not Finn's hounds; and she stepped back, afraid.

'It is many months that I have waited for you, Sav, daughter of Bov,' he said. And she saw that it was the dark immortal who loved her, and she gave a great cry and turned to fly back to the safety of the stronghold. But he struck her with a wand, and instantly she became a hind, as before. Desperately she made for the gate, but the two hounds headed her back. Twisting and evading them, she tried time after time to escape, but ever they and the enchanter were between her and safety.

Hearing her cry, Finn's servants came to the gate and saw with terror the dreadful transformation. Shouting to each other and seizing any weapons to hand, they ran down the hillside towards her; but by the time they reached her, they could no longer see her. Nor was there any sign of the dark immortal or the hounds, save only a great trampling of flying feet on the grass about them, and the baying of hounds all around, sounding first on one side and then on the other. The servants ran here and there, striking wildly at the empty air, until the noise of the chase died away in the distance and all was silent save for the sound of their own panting breath and their weeping.

As he had promised, Finn and the Fianna drove away the men of Lochlann speedily, and it was no more than eight days after he had left home that Finn rode back again. But, climbing the Hill of Allen, he looked in vain for the expected sight of Sav waiting on the ramparts.

When he learnt what had befallen, Finn said no word, but went silently to his own chamber, and there he remained for two days, seeing no one. On the third day he came out and once again, for a time, took part in the life of the stronghold, ordering his household as before. But after that, for seven years, taking with him no hounds but Bran and Skolaun, he searched every hill and glen, every wood and heath, every cave and lakeside in Ireland, seeking Sav: but he never found her. Then, at the end of seven years, he returned home and took up his old life again, directing the affairs of the Fianna, hunting, and fighting against Ireland's enemies.

One day when Finn was hunting on the slopes of Ben Gulban, in Sligo, with other leaders of the Fianna, they were all startled to hear a strange whimpering from the hounds. Hurrying to see what was amiss, they found, in the shadow of a rock, a young boy standing with the hounds all around him, and Bran and Skolaun standing, one on either side of him, snapping and growling at the other hounds when they came too close.

The boy appeared some seven or eight years old. He was naked and he could not understand them when they spoke to him; nor did he seem to have the habit of speech, but only stood there, staring at them gravely and unafraid, as they gathered round. And his long hair was yellow, the colour of Finn's hair, so that Finn gazed at him for many moments, full of thought.

They took him with them to their hunting-camp and gave him food and clothing; and when Finn returned to Allen, he took the boy with him. In time he learnt to speak and told Finn his story: how he had known no father, and no mother save only a hind with whom he had dwelt in a pleasant valley. 'No one came there to us,' he said, 'but only a tall, dark man, who would appear and speak with the hind. Sometimes he spoke gently and sometimes he spoke harshly, but always she shrank away from him in fear. And then there came a day when the dark man spoke with her for many hours, at first kindly, and then in anger. And then at last he struck her with a wand and she went away with him, turning sadly to look at me until she was out of sight. I tried to run after them, but I could not move; and in a while I fell to the ground and knew no more until I awoke alone on Ben Gulban where you found me. Oh, how I searched for the valley where I had lived with the hind: but I never reached it. And then you came, with your friends and your hounds.'

'That hind was indeed your mother,' said Finn quietly, when the boy had finished his story. 'She was Sav, my wife.'

Finn called his son Oisin—Little Fawn—and he grew up into a great warrior and an even greater poet. He was the bard of the Fianna and he sang of their fame and their glorious deeds, that all men might hear of these things.

Oisin was the father of the brave youth Oscar, whom his grand-father Finn loved above all others. Ever rash in combat, Oscar was slain in the battle of Gavra, fighting against the leader of the enemy, and Finn wept long for him.

After this, one day when Finn and the Fianna were hunting all about the Lakes of Killarney, on the shore of Lough Leane they were aware of a maiden riding towards them on a snow-white horse, where, a moment before, there had been neither rider nor horse. She was clad like a queen, in a cloak set with red stars, with a golden crown on her head. Lightly and proudly she sat on the back of her huge white horse, which was shod with bright gold. The Fianna all stared at her with wonder; but none with greater wonder than Oisin, who watched her entranced.

Finn came forward and greeted her, asking her name, and she answered, 'I am Niav of the Golden Hair, the daughter of Manannan, god of the sea, and I have come from my father's kingdom, the Land of the Ever Young, for love of your son Oisin. For your son's fame, Finn Mac Cool, and the fame of the songs that he makes, have reached even to the homes of the immortals.' She turned to Oisin. 'Oisin, son of Finn, I have travelled a long way in search of you. Will you come back with me to the Land of the Ever Young? It is a fair land, Oisin, where the trees bear blossom and fruit together, and there are green leaves all the year round. In my land I will give you a coat of mail which no weapon can pierce and a sword which cannot miss a stroke. There you will never grow old, or lose your strength, or die; and there sorrow will be unknown to you. And I shall be your wife, Oisin, in the Land of the Ever Young. Will you come with me?'

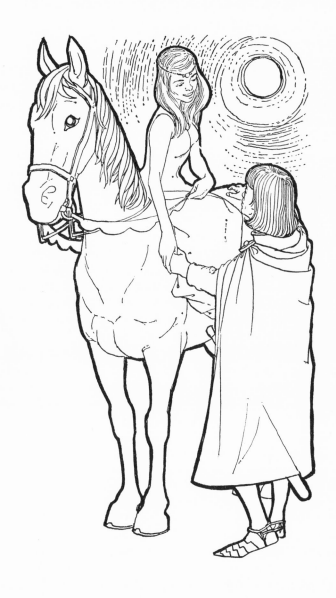

Like one under a spell, Oisin stepped forward and laid his hand over her white hand as it held the horse's reins. He looked up into her eyes. 'Niav of the Golden Hair, I will follow you to the Land of the Ever Young, or anywhere else you please.'

Finn cried out in distress, 'Do not leave us, my son, for, if you do, we shall never see you again.'

But Oisin did not seem to understand his words. As in a dream, he smiled at Finn and his comrades in farewell, then mounted the white horse behind Niav. She immediately turned the horse's head, and it galloped away from them, towards the coast of Ireland, growing ever smaller in the distance. Long did Finn and the others strain their eyes after Oisin, whom they were never to see again.

When the white horse came to the sea, it galloped lightly over the waves, until Oisin knew no longer whether they were on dry land or on water. A mist came all about them, and in the mist he saw strange shapes, towers and houses and cities; a fawn which seemed to be running over the waves, and a white hound with one red ear after it; a maiden on a bay horse, with a golden apple in her hand, and a warrior riding after her in a mantle of yellow silk. This and many other dreamlike shapes did Oisin see as they went.

'Tell me,' he said wonderingly to Niav, 'what are all these marvels about us?'

She laughed. 'Marvels they may seem to you now, Oisin, but they are as nothing to the marvels of my father's land.'

At length they came to a wild, storm-tossed stretch of sea; but though the wind howled above them and the waves towered high on every side, the enchanted white horse galloped on, while the lightning flashed and the thunder rolled. At last they were past the region of storm, and the sea lay before them calm and blue, and in the distance, ever drawing nearer, was the coastline of a fair land. On the shore of this land they dismounted.

'What is this place, Niav?' asked Oisin, marvelling.

'This is the Land of the Ever Young, and there is none of those delights which I have promised you, that you will not enjoy here.'

As Oisin looked about him in wonder, scores of people came hurrying to meet them; and all were beautiful and young and gay. In a palace of shining marble studded with every precious stone, Manannan

Mac Lir welcomed him. 'Greetings to you, Oisin, son of Finn. Much have we heard of the deeds which you have performed, and long have we known your songs. Sing now for us, the joyful and deathless, instead of for mortals who suffer and die. Take my daughter as your bride and live in happiness for ever.'

Oisin found that it was the truth which Niav had spoken. In the Land of the Ever Young the sand was more golden, the sky more blue, the flowers of brighter and more varied colours, and the songs of the birds sweeter, than ever these things had been in Ireland. In the palace there were silken carpets and dishes of gold, food and wine richer than any earthly meat and drink, fountains which sparkled in the sunlight that was brighter than the sunlight of Ireland had ever been. And to Oisin it all seemed good, and he could not imagine a time when he would grow weary of it.

The feasting for the marriage of Oisin and Niav lasted for ten days— and joyous days they were. Many days as joyous followed them for Oisin and his golden-haired bride, living in a fair palace in the Land of the Ever Young.

But there came a day when, in the midst of the delights around him, Oisin suddenly remembered the long days of hunting which he had spent with his father Finn and the leaders of the Fianna. In his mind he saw for a second the plains of Ireland, purple with heather, and the bracken, all golden in the autumn, and he heard in his memory the sound of Finn's hunting-call, and he seemed to smell for an instant the smoke of the fires as the Fianna cooked in the evening the deer which they had killed; and there was a momentary sorrow at his heart. It was gone almost as soon as he knew it was there; but it returned again another day—and lasted longer; and yet again—and lasted longer still. And then it was returning often and often, and each time the feeling of sorrow became a little deeper and his longing grew a little stronger, until the perfection of his life in the Land of the Ever Young seemed flat and stale and he took no more joy in it.

Then, when he had been, as it seemed to him, in that land for three years, he said to Niav, 'I am sick with longing to see once again the hills and glens of Ireland, to speak once more with my father Finn and my friends among the Fianna. Let me go to them for only a little time and I shall come back to you restored.'

Niav was silent for a long while, before she finally spoke.

Then she said, 'Go, Oisin; though I fear that if you do, I shall never see you again.'

'But I shall return to you, Niav. I go only to greet Finn and my comrades, and to tell them of my great happiness here with you. It will only be a little time before we are together again.'

Niav shook her head. 'I have fears of this journey, Oisin. You will not find Finn and the Fianna as you left them, and Ireland will be changed.'

Oisin laughed. 'Three years is too short a time for Ireland to change; and far too short a time for Finn and my friends to forget me, or to become other than they have always been.'

'You do not understand my words,' said Niav. 'How could you? But only remember this, and all will be well: do not dismount from the white horse, or you will not come back to me. A second time I say it: do not set your feet on the green grass of Ireland, or you will never return to this land. Oh, my dearest husband, a third time I say it: if you dismount from the white horse, you will never see me again.'

Oisin took her in his arms and kissed her. 'I shall remember what you have said and I shall come back to you,' he promised.

He mounted the enchanted white horse and it carried him to the sea and over the sea; and many marvels he saw on the way, before at last the horse reached Ireland, with Oisin's heart singing in his breast.

But from the shore Ireland did not seem the same as he remembered it; and he saw no sign of the Fianna, but only strange, small folk toiling in the fields or riding little horses. And he marvelled at it, for they were not like the people he had known; and he became suddenly afraid of what he would hear if he asked them for news of Finn.

Ireland was indeed changed. Gone were the places he knew and in vain he searched for them. In vain he listened for the hunting-cry of the Fianna echoing in the hills. In vain he sought out the homes of those men of the Fianna who had lived near the coast.

He turned the horse's head and made haste to the Hill of Allen; but when he came there, instead of Finn's stronghold standing firm and sure, there were only the heather-covered slopes of the hill, with a few cattle grazing, and here and there a grassy mound or a stone overgrown with moss and weeds. Appalled, he stared at the desolation.

'What enemy could have been strong enough to do this to my father Finn?' he whispered. He sought out some of the small, mean folk who now dwelt in Ireland and called to them, asking for news of Finn.

'It is one of the gods of old come back to earth,' they muttered and crossed themselves.

'Tell me,' he said, 'where is Finn Mac Cool?'

'Finn Mac Cool died long ago. He was a great hero in the old days,' one answered him.

'He had a son named Oisin who rode away with an enchantress, three hundred years ago,' said another.

A third said wonderingly, 'From what is said of them, Finn and the men of old must have looked much like you, tall stranger.'

Then the terrible truth was clear to Oisin, and he remembered the words of Niav, that he would not find things as they had been; and in horror he galloped away.

Throughout Ireland he rode, still seeking for a trace of Finn: though he knew it was vain. Then, near the sea on the eastern coast, at Glanismole, where he had often hunted with the Fianna, he came upon a group of men who were trying to raise a large, flat stone from the ground. When they saw him approaching, they ran to him and begged his help. 'For you look tall and strong, like a giant,' they said.

'Truly,' he thought, 'what poor, feeble folk they are. That stone, why, Oscar would have taken it up in one hand and flung it right over their heads.' Pitying them, he rode up, and bending down, took hold of the great slab and heaved it out of their way.

The men shouted out their praises for his strength and crowded round him, saying that the gods were come back to Ireland. But with the strain of lifting the stone, the girth of the saddle had broken, and to save himself from falling, Oisin jumped to the ground. No sooner had his two feet touched the earth of Ireland than the horse gave a shrill neigh and faded like a mist, and Oisin himself became an old man, with long white hair and a long white beard, frail and withered, half sightless and groping. The men fled in terror and watched him from a distance; but, little by little, they crept back again and spoke to him. 'Who are you, stranger?'

'I am Oisin, son of Finn Mac Cool.'

Bolder now, they laughed, thinking that they had imagined that they had earlier seen a strong young man on a horse. 'You are old, stranger, but even you are not old enough for that. Finn Mac Cool and the Fianna have been gone three hundred years. Now we have holy Patrick, who preaches to us and prays for us that we may be saved from the fires of hell.'

'I do not know of what you are talking,' said Oisin wearily.

They carried him to a house and cared for him; and word of the strange thing that had happened that day, and of the name that he had called himself, came to the ears of Patrick the Christian, and he sent for Oisin and took him into his house and told him about the new faith and sang psalms to him; for he knew it would be a great triumph for his faith if he were able to convert the last of the Fianna.

But Oisin—whose remembrance of Niav and the Land of the Ever Young had grown dim and vague, though his memories of Finn and the Fianna were sharp and clear and ever present—Oisin said, 'I have listened to far sweeter music than your psalms, Patrick. I have heard the song of the blackbird of Letterlee, and the thrush singing in Glenascail; and I have heard the cry of Finn's hounds as they gave chase, and the music of the Dord-Fiann. Cease your psalms and let me be.' He sighed. 'Oh, it is sad, Patrick, to be left alone after all the Fianna have gone, a poor, old, blind man.'

'Forget about the Fianna, Oisin, and think instead of heaven,' urged Patrick.

'If this heaven of which you have told me is such a fine house in which to live, then, worthy Patrick, ask your god to take Finn and the Fianna to live in it, for they were great and good men.'

'I will not ask heaven for Finn and the Fianna,' said Patrick firmly, 'for, indeed, they were not good men.'

Oisin shook his head. 'You are wrong. They were brave and generous and hospitable, and they are a great loss to Ireland and to all the world. Oh, had you known Finn and the Fianna, Patrick, you would have left your god and your psalms to go hunting with them.'

'Neither Finn's courage nor the gold which he gave away will avail him now, for he and all the Fianna are in bondage in hell, sorrowing in the house of pain.'

'You lie, Patrick,' exclaimed Oisin. 'There is no one anywhere who could hold Finn against his will. If the Clan Baskin were with him, or the Clan Morna—Finn would be free. If Dermot alone were there, or Gaul Mac Morna, or Oscar, my son—Finn would be free.'

'Not all the Fianna who ever lived could bring Finn out of hell, Oisin.'

Indignantly Oisin said, 'What harm did Finn ever do to your god, that he should keep him in hell?'

'Finn paid no heed to God, Oisin, and that is why he is in hell. Now cease your foolish ranting and remember that you, too, like the Fianna, shall sorrow in hell very soon.'

'If I were not the only one left, you would not dare to threaten me, O joyless man, but newly come to Ireland. Were even Conan the Bald alive, you would not growl at me for long.'

'Come now, Oisin,' said Patrick more gently, 'you have little time left to you, think only of God, and He will take you into heaven.'

Oisin was silent for a time, then he said, 'Patrick, since you know these things, tell me, would your god let me have hounds with me in heaven?'

'Foolish old man!' exclaimed Patrick, exasperated. 'Can you not forget the world, you who are so near to leaving it?'

Oisin paid no heed to his rebuke, but said, 'If I were to meet with your god and I had my hound with me, if your god gave me hospitality, surely I could persuade him to feed my hound also.'

Still angry, Patrick cried out at this, and Oisin said thoughtfully, 'The more I listen to you, Patrick, and the more I hear of your god, the surer I am that any one of the Fianna was better than either of you.'

'How can you speak so!' exclaimed Patrick, appalled. 'It would be better to have God for one hour, than to have all the Fianna of Ireland for ever. You are old and foolish, Oisin, and it is a sorry thing for you to be always talking of the Fianna when you are nearing your end. You have gone astray at the close of your life and you stand between the straight path and the crooked. Come on to the straight path, Oisin, and it will lead you to God's angels and to heaven.'

'From what you have told me of heaven, Patrick, I think that I would rather have the deer leaping on the hills and the badgers roaming in the valleys, than all the delights of heaven which you offer me,' said Oisin drily.

Day after day Patrick talked and argued with Oisin, sometimes threatening him and sometimes cajoling, and never quite losing hope of converting him. 'Come, Oisin,' he said once, 'I think that you will yet forsake the remembrance of the Fianna and walk at last with God in heaven.'

But at that Oisin became angry in his turn. 'Do you dare to say that I would forsake my friends? I would never forsake Finn or the Fianna. And as for their being in hell—why, Patrick, they would never be anywhere where they did not wish to be. And as for your god—were I to see my son Oscar wrestling with your god, and were I to see Oscar thrown down, I would say that your god was strong. But how could he be stronger than Finn, who was a brave and generous man without any fault? Were there a place, above or below, better than heaven, Finn and all the Fianna would be there. That I know. Ask your god, Patrick, whether he has ever seen, in any place, men to equal the Fianna. We of the Fianna were ever brave and we never lied. There is not one of your priests, Patrick—however sweetly they sing their psalms—who is truer to his word than were the Fianna; and there is not one of your priests, Patrick, who is more hospitable than Finn. Ask your god, Patrick, whether he has ever seen, in any place, men to equal the Fianna.'

'The Fianna may have been all these things, Oisin, but they have passed like a mist and now lie in pain, powerless. God, who is my king, made the heavens and the world; it is He who gives strength to the warrior; it is He who makes the trees and the flowers, the moon and the stars; it is He who puts fish in the rivers and grass in the fields.'

Oisin laughed a little. 'Oh, Patrick, those deeds may be well enough for your god, but Finn would have taken no delight in them. Finn's joy was in fighting and hunting, in eating and drinking, in swimming and playing at chess, in listening to poets and in giving gold.'

'And for this, Oisin, he is now in hell, and all the Fianna with him,' said Patrick quickly.

'If that is so, then great is the shame of it to your god, that he does not release Finn,' said Oisin indignantly. 'Were your god in bonds in a house of pain, then Finn would fight to release him, for Finn was ever generous and kind. He left no man to suffer pain or distress, but gave him gold or fought for him, until his troubles were over.'

'Cease from such foolishness, Oisin, and cease from mocking

God,' said Patrick sternly. 'Honour Him and pray to Him and He will yet pardon you your sins.'

'I will offer no amends to you or to your god for what I have done that displeases you both; and I would give you no thanks for pardon, either. And let me tell you this, Patrick from Rome, of the harsh faith, if in the days that are left to me, you hear me crying aloud or see me weeping, it will not be to your god or for my sins, but because Finn and the Fianna are gone and I am left alone. Now let me be, Patrick. As I have lived, so shall I die.'

★   ★   ★

Strangely enough, though the tradition of Oisin in the Land of the Ever Young is very ancient, we have no written account of his adventures there earlier than the poem ascribed to Michael Comyn and written about 1749, which is based on the old tales of the storytellers.

There exists a group of legends telling how Keelta, head of the Clan Ronan, and the fastest runner amongst the Fianna, also survived into Christian times; but Keelta, unlike Oisin, was converted by Patrick whose good friend he became.

The collection of mediaeval ballads usually known as The Dialogues of Oisin and Patrick, *from which I have taken the last part of the story of Oisin, show a remarkable tolerance and an unexpected sympathy with Oisin's point of view. The dignity of Oisin's loyalty and his loving regrets for his friends are a fitting close to the great cycle of legends concerning Finn and the Fianna: tales so many of which were already old when the Christian tales were new.*

In lands where they spread their recent faith, the early fathers of the Christian Church fixed their main festivals at those times of the year when the great pagan religious festivals were held: Christmas at the season of the midwinter festival; Easter and its message of resurrection at the ancient seed-sowing time, that season when spring returns to the world, arising again out of the darkness of winter.

A number of the old gods were adopted, with necessary changes, into the Christian Church, as saints; but even after two thousand years some of them can be recognized for what they once were. Of all such transmutations perhaps the most obvious of all is an Irish saint, St Bridget, honoured in England as

St Bride. Even her name is almost unaltered—Brigit, daughter of the Dagda, sister to Angus and Midir. St Bridget's symbol is a flame, in remembrance of the flame which shone above her on the day she took the veil; and the house where she lived is said to have burst into a pillar of fire which reached to heaven; while a sacred flame was kept alight incessantly at her shrine in Kildare—circumstances which may all be considered very fitting for the one-time goddess of fire.

8

THE VOYAGE OF MAELDUN

Tales of marvellous voyages were very popular with the old Irish story-tellers and their listeners; and the voyage of Maeldun, son of Ailell, is probably the earliest of them all. Maeldun's adventures make even the tallest of travellers' tall tales seem credible by comparison.

★   ★   ★

There once lived in the south-west of Ireland, at Dooclone, near the sea, in the land of the people of Owen, a chieftain named Ailell of the Edge of Battle. One day, when most of his men were away from home, hunting or the like, a band of fierce raiders from one of the islands off the coast landed on the shore and began to lay waste the country around Dooclone. Ailell, with all the warriors he could muster, went boldly to meet them to try and drive them away; but the raiders were too many for him, and all his men were slain and he himself was forced to flee into the church for safety. But the raiders came after him and burnt the church, and him with it; then, unhindered, they carried off cattle and grain, stowed it in their ship and set sail.

Not long after his death, a son was born to a nun whom Ailell had made captive—and later released—one time when, with the king, he had been taking part in a foray on neighbouring territory. Wishing to conceal the birth of the child, the nun sent him secretly to her dear friend, the queen, whose husband ruled the people of Owen in what is today the County Clare. The king and queen gladly took the son of Ailell of the Edge of Battle and brought him up as their child, along with their own three boys; the four of them sharing the same cradle, cared for by the same nurse, and drinking from the same cup.

Maeldun, as they called Ailell's son, grew to be a tall and handsome youth, excelling in all sports and games; so that he was soon accounted —and rightly—by far the best of all the youths in the king's house, for he easily outstripped them in every race, beat them at every sport, rode and wrestled—and even played chess—better than any other of his years. He was much loved for his generosity and the goodwill he showed to all; but because of his many talents there were those amongst the other youths who were envious of him.

One day Maeldun overheard one of his companions say bitterly to another, 'How shameful it is for us, the sons of the lords of the people of Owen, to have to admit ourselves worsted in everything by Maeldun, a lad of lowly birth, who does not even know the name of his father or mother.'

Up till that moment Maeldun had believed that he was the son of the king and queen and, greatly distressed, he went to the queen. 'Today I heard it said that I am not your son. If this be so, then tell me who my parents were, for I shall neither eat nor drink until I know the truth.'

The queen was troubled for his sake, and she said, 'Pay no heed to the words of a jealous rival. Have I not been a good mother to you? Is there in all Ireland a mother who loves her son better than I love you?'

'That is so,' he said. 'Yet tell me who my parents were, for I shall have no happiness until I know the truth.'

So the queen took Maeldun to his mother, saying, 'This is your true mother. Ask her what you would know.'

'It can bring you neither happiness nor advantage, my son, nor indeed anything better than you have already, to know the name of your father,' said his mother.

'Nevertheless,' said he, 'I would know his name.'

'Your father was the chieftain Ailell of the Edge of Battle, of Dooclone, and he died before you were born.'

Upon this Maeldun determined to go and see for himself where his father had lived, and taking leave of the king and the queen, and of his mother, he set off; and his three foster-brothers, the king's sons, went with him.

When the folk at Dooclone learnt that he was the son of Ailell of the Edge of Battle, they gave him a great welcome, and his companions likewise, so that Maeldun was pleased and thought he had done well to persist in his enquiry after the truth of his birth; and he remained several days in Dooclone.

But one morning, when he and his foster-brothers, together with some other youths, were playing with a large stone, seeing who could throw it farthest over the charred ruins of a burnt building, a carping, evil-tongued fellow who stood near by said spitefully, 'You would do better to busy yourself avenging the man who was burnt to death in this place, rather than to be playing at casting stones over his dead bones.'

Maeldun stopped his play. 'What man was that?' he asked.

'Ailell of the Edge of Battle, our chieftain, your father,' the man replied.

'Who killed him?' asked Maeldun.

'Raiders who came from the sea in a ship,' said the man, and added, 'And those same raiders are still sailing in that same ship today.'

At that Maeldun dropped the stone he held, wrapped his cloak about him and went away thoughtfully, without another word.

The next day he began to ask everyone where the raiders might be found, and after much questioning he learnt that they lived on an island a good distance from the mainland, and that there was no way of reaching them except by sea. Then he went to seek counsel of a wise man who lived near Dooclone, for he had determined to build himself a ship and sail in search of the raiders and avenge his father's death.

The wise man consulted omens and portents and told Maeldun what he should do: how he should build his ship, which days were the most propitious for the building, and on which day he should set sail; and he bade him most particularly to take with him, as his crew, neither more nor less than seventeen men.

Maeldun at once began to build his ship; and soon it was ready, so willingly he had worked. Then he went all about his foster-father's kingdom, finding adventurous and bold-spirited youths who would accompany him on his voyage; and at last he had found them, to the number of seventeen, and was ready to set sail. And among his crew were his two best friends, Germaun and Diuran. Then, having bidden farewell to his mother and to the king and queen, on the day named by the wise man he put out to sea.

But the ship had only gone a little way from the shore when Maeldun heard voices hailing him, and looking back, he saw his three foster-brothers running down the sands, signing to him to turn back and take them on board. 'You must not go without us,' they shouted to him.

'I was long enough finding my crew,' Maeldun shouted back to them. 'You had time to make up your minds before this. I have all the crew I was bidden to take, so you cannot come with me. It would bring us ill luck.'

But they insisted, crying out, 'We will swim after the ship, if you do not turn back for us.' And with that they threw themselves into the water and swam out to sea.

Thereupon, since he could not let them drown, Maeldun was forced to turn his ship and take them aboard, though he knew no good could come of ignoring the wise man's words.

They sailed in the direction of the island of the raiders; and after ⟨sailing⟩ for two days, at midnight on the second night they came in ⟨to⟩ a small island with a large house on it, standing close by the

'We shall spend tonight on dry land,' they said, well pleased. 'Let us hope we are offered a good welcome, late though it is.'

'Listen,' said one of them. They fell silent and heard from the house the sounds of revelry and laughter coming clearly to them over the water. 'There should be a good enough welcome there, from the sound of it,' they said; and carefully through the darkness they made their way to the shore.

They were about to beach the ship, when suddenly, out from the house there came two men, intent on settling a quarrel. Drunken and boastful, they were bragging and reviling each other; and listening to them, Maeldun and the others heard one of the men shout out, 'You can keep your hands off me, for I am a better warrior than you. It was I, not you or any other man, who slew Ailell of the Edge of Battle and burnt him in Dooclone all those years ago. And from that day to this, no one has dared to avenge him. Have you ever done such a deed as that?'

Germaun and Diuran, overjoyed, whispered to Maeldun, 'What fortune! After only two days' sailing, to have found what we came to seek. Our enemies are as good as in our hands already, and their house destroyed.'

But even as they spoke, a great wind arose and a storm was upon them and they were blown away from the shore, buffeted and tossed by the waves, and driven far from the island and right out to sea. And by the time that the storm had died down, during the next day, they were many miles from Ireland and had not the slightest knowledge of where in all the wide ocean they might be.

'There is nothing we can do save take down the sail and lay aside the oars and drift where fate wills,' said Maeldun. 'And may we soon sight land.' He turned to his foster-brothers. 'It is thanks to you that this evil has come upon us. The wise man bade me take with me no more and no less than seventeen men.'

His foster-brothers could give him no answer, for they knew his rebuke to be just.

For three days and three nights they drifted before the wind without sighting land. Their stores were running low and they were growing anxious. But towards dawn on the fourth day, before it was light, they heard to the north-east the sound of waves breaking on a shore.

Germaun cried out joyfully, 'Listen! We must be close to land.'

As soon as it was light enough, they saw an island near by and made for it with all speed, watching warily for signs of human habitation. They noticed none; yet they had no wish to venture ashore rashly.

'It would be best if only one or two of us were to make the landing first,' said Maeldun. 'Let us draw lots to decide who shall go.' But even as they were doing so, the look-out man gave a cry and pointed to the island. The others looked up and saw a number of ants, each one as big as a well-grown foal, coming down to the edge of the sea, their great eyes fixed eagerly upon the approaching ship and their sharp jaws snapping.

'It would not surprise me if those ants had a mind to break their fast off us,' said one of the crew doubtfully. And all the others echoed his words.

'Let us make haste away from here,' cried Maeldun. 'It is far better to go hungry oneself than to satisfy the hunger of a monstrous ant.'

So they turned the ship and sailed away as fast as they were able.

They tightened their belts and sailed onwards without sight of land for another three days and three nights; and on the fourth day they reached another island. On this island, also, there seemed to be no men; but it was thickly wooded, with tall trees, and on every tree perched scores of birds with bright plumage. Hungry as they were, remembering the ants, they approached the island cautiously, but saw nothing to alarm them and no sign of life save the birds. They would have urged Maeldun to draw lots again to see which of them should venture on shore, but he said, 'There is no need of that. I will go myself.'

Several of the company immediately offered to go with him, and they landed carefully and walked slowly up the beach. But nothing harmed them, and they found it easy enough to kill a great number of the birds and carry them on board. After they had eaten, they sailed on more cheerfully.

A few days later they had a fortunate escape from a monster much like a horse in shape, but with legs like the legs of a dog and long, sharp, blue claws. This terrifying creature hurled great rocks at their ship as they sailed by his island, so that they were lucky to pass it alive.

After sighting several more islands and having a narrow escape or two, very weary and hungry they came to an island with nothing on it but a single apple tree, so huge that its branches spread not only over all the island, but out over the sea as well. As they passed beneath one of these branches, Maeldun leapt upwards and caught it in his hands, and as the ship moved on, he let the branch slip through his hands until, at the very end of the branch, he was able to pick three apples. Three apples might seem very little for one and twenty hungry sailors; but the tree must certainly have been enchanted, because each of the apples was food and drink enough for all of them for forty days; and Maeldun and his companions blessed the chance that had taken them past the island of the apple tree.

A few more strange places they passed—including an island where grew numberless fine fruit trees amongst which walked and grazed strange, fiery animals, shaped much like pigs, but burning like molten copper—before they sighted a small island upon which stood a tall white palace. By this time their store of apples was eaten, and weary and sick of the sight of the sea, they hoped that here, at last, might be human company, a welcome for weary voyagers, and good cheer.

They landed boldly and walked into the palace. But the great building seemed deserted, though it showed no signs of neglect. From room to room they went, meeting no living creature until, in the very centre of the palace, they came to a great hall beautifully furnished with couches spread with white, soft rugs, and tables laden with food: roasted pork and a boiled ox, good bread, and drinking-horns in plenty, well filled.

Around the walls of this hall there were hanging magnificent treasures of gold and silver: a row of brooches, a row of jewelled collars and a row of gold-hilted swords. In this room, also, stood four low marble pillars, and jumping in play from the top of one pillar to another was a small cat. When they entered the hall, the cat paused in its game to glance at them, then, paying them no further heed, continued to leap from top to top of the pillars.

After they had wandered about the hall, marvelling at its wonders, Maeldun spoke with courtesy to the cat. 'Is it for us that this feast has been prepared?'

The cat stood still and looked at Maeldun for a moment, then turned away to its play once more.

'It must be that the food is for us,' said Maeldun. 'Let us sit down and enjoy it, my friends.'

They ate and drank their fill, and then lay down to sleep on the couches. In the morning, when they awoke, they breakfasted; then they gathered together all that was left of the food and the ale, that they might take it with them to the ship. As they were leaving the palace, grateful for their night's entertainment and rest, Maeldun's eldest foster-brother looked longingly at the jewels on the wall. 'Shall I bring away one of those collars with me?' he whispered to Maeldun.

Maeldun exclaimed at his suggestion. 'How could you think of such a thing?' he said. 'We have had food and rest and the best entertainment since we left Ireland. It would be shameful indeed to steal from the little cat who has been our host.'

But the king's son would not listen to Maeldun. Instead he went to the wall and took down one of the largest of the jewelled collars and hurried out after the others. But he was hardly halfway across the outer courtyard when the cat was upon him. Like a blazing arrow of fire the cat passed right through the young man's body, leaving him a heap of smouldering ashes on the ground. Then the cat returned to the hall, and leaping to the top of one of the pillars, sat there quietly.

Horrified, the others stood and stared; and Maeldun, white and shaken, turned back and picked up the jewelled collar, and returning into the hall, spoke soothingly to the cat before hanging the collar up in its place on the wall. Then from the courtyard he collected the ashes of his foster-brother and strewed them on the beach. Mourning for their lost comrade, the rest of them put out to sea and sailed away from the strange palace of the cat.

Some days later they reached a large island on which, not too far from the coast, stood a high hill. Wanting to view the farther side of the island, Maeldun decided to send two men to climb the hill. His friends, Germaun and Diuran, offered to go, and they set off together.

On the way they came to a broad, shallow river and sat down on the bank to rest their legs, having been unused, for so many days, to much walking. Idly, Germaun dipped the head of his spear into the river, and to his horror, the head, and all of the shaft which had touched the water, burnt off, as though it had been thrust into a fire.

'I think it were best that we went no farther into this country,' they said, looking about them fearfully. Suddenly they saw, on the opposite side of the river, a herd of huge beasts, like enormous hornless oxen, all lying motionless on the ground.

'Are they real?' asked Germaun. 'Or are they no more than rocks resembling cattle?' And when Diuran had no answer for him, he struck loudly with his spear-shaft on his shield to rouse them.

Instantly a huge giant leapt to his feet from amongst the cattle and shouted in an earth-shaking voice, 'Why are you frightening my poor little calves?'

Germaun, astounded at being told that such huge beasts were no more than small calves, gasped, 'If those are calves, where are the cows?'

The giant pointed. 'Up there on the hill, grazing.'

Germaun and Diuran gave one look at each other and then, without another word, turned and ran for the shore.

Some days after this, Maeldun and his company reached an island upon which they could see, as they came near, a number of men and women all garbed in black and wailing. All about the island these people walked, wringing their hands and sighing, never once pausing to rest.

Maeldun and the others were puzzled by this, and they determined to find out what grief it was that could so affect a whole island. This time it fell to the lot of Maeldun's second foster-brother to go ashore, which he did with great curiosity. But as soon as he came amongst the mourners, he, too, began to wail and weep; and he would not return to his companions, though they called to him from the ship. Thereupon Maeldun sent two other men to fetch him back; but it was the same with them; no sooner were they amongst the folk of the island than they began, like them, to mourn.

'This is a pretty plight, indeed,' said Maeldun, and thought earnestly for a while. Then he called to four other men and bade them go to fetch their comrades. 'But take care,' he said, 'that whilst doing so you do not breathe the air of the island, for I fear there is something most strange about it. Put your cloaks closely about yourselves, covering your mouths and noses, and look neither at the earth nor at the sky, and neither to the right of you nor to the left; but only look steadily at your comrades and take hold of them and bring them quickly back with you.'

This the men did; and in that way they were able to rescue the two men who had gone immediately before them; though they had a hard struggle to drag them back to the ship, weeping and wailing all the way. But of the king's second son they could see no trace.

The moment they were on board again, the two men ceased their mourning, and their companions gathered round them, questioning them. 'What did you see to make you weep so?' they asked.

'Why, nothing,' replied the two men. 'We do not know why we wept. All we know is that everyone else was weeping, and so we did likewise.'

Maeldun waited in vain for his foster-brother, but there was no sign of him; and at last, for fear of losing more men by landing to search for him, he put out to sea, leaving behind him, with many regrets, the king's second son.

Many other strange islands they passed in the days which followed. There was one where they found food which looked like cheese, yet tasted like whatever best pleased the man who ate it; another which was spanned by a crystal bridge leading to a palace; and another on which lived great numbers of birds, all of which spoke with the voices of men.

Soon after they saw the talking birds they had a further narrow escape from destruction. Having sighted an island, they were approaching it when they heard a loud noise as of a hammer striking on an anvil and a smith's bellows roaring—but all far louder than the sounds of any smithy they had ever known. When they were a little closer, they saw three giant smiths hard at work hammering a mass of glowing iron on an anvil. Their huge voices reached quite clearly to the men on the ship.

'Are they near yet?' asked one.

'Hush, hold your tongue,' said another. 'They will hear you.'

'Who is it you can see coming?' asked the third.

'Some very little men sailing in a toy boat.'

'Wait until they are a little closer.' The giant smiths chuckled together as though in anticipation of a good jest.

Maeldun said hastily, 'We must go from here with all speed; but they must not see that we are going, or they will attack us at once. Do not turn the ship, but row backwards as fast as you can.'

The crew did this, while Maeldun listened anxiously for the big voices of the giants. And, as he had expected, soon he heard one ask, 'Are they near enough yet?'

'They do not seem to be coming closer, so they must be resting on their oars, for they have not turned their foolish little boat.'

'Then we, also, can wait.'

A little time later the first giant asked again, 'What are they doing now?'

After a pause the other giant replied, 'I think that they must be flying from us, for they seem to be farther off.'

'Then let us wait no longer,' cried the first giant, and he came running out of the forge holding a huge mass of red-hot iron in his tongs. This he flung straight at the ship. But, thanks to Maeldun's quick wits, the ship was by that time too far away, and the iron fell short. And though the sea hissed and steamed and bubbled about the hot iron, the ship, rocking on the boiling water, came safely away.

More marvels they saw after this: a land beneath the waves, glimpsed through the clear water; a stream of water rising up in the air and arching down again like a rainbow; and a tall, eight-sided, silver pillar standing up from the sea. From the top of this pillar—so high that they could not see it—there hung down to the sea a vast silver net. The meshes of this net were so large that their ship was able to sail right through a single one of them. As they passed through the mesh, Diuran drew his sword and hacked off a piece of the net.

'Do not destroy the net, Diuran,' protested Maeldun, 'for it is the work of some great craftsman.'

'I am not destroying the net, Maeldun,' said Diuran cheerfully. 'I am only taking a keepsake, so that people will believe me when I tell them the story of our adventures, when we are home again.'

After this they came to an island which was balanced at the top of a pillar. They could not stop at this island, for there was nowhere to land; so they were obliged to sail on, and soon they came to a very large island on which there stood a strong fortress with a fair city about it. There was a good harbour on this island, so they landed and went ashore and were greeted kindly by a number of women. To their surprise, they learnt that there were no men in this city, but only the queen and her seventeen daughters.

The queen made them welcome and gave a feast in their honour, and the next day she said to them, 'It is a hard life to be always wandering about the ocean. Stay here with me in my land and take your ease and be happy. Each of you can have as a wife one of my seventeen daughters, and Maeldun shall be my husband. Here you will always be young and beautiful, for there is no old age or sickness in my realm.'

And because the winter was upon them, Maeldun agreed to stay for a while; but he soon found life on the island so pleasant that he was ready to stay there for ever. For the three months of winter they remained ashore; and though for Maeldun, who spent each day in the company of the lovely queen, the time passed quickly enough, to his comrades it seemed like three years.

'We are homesick,' they complained to him. 'It is time we tried to find our way back to Ireland, since it seems we shall never find the raiders who slew your father.'

'There is nothing in Ireland better than we have here,' said Maeldun.

They murmured amongst themselves at this, saying, 'It is plain enough that Maeldun has fallen in love with the queen of this place. Very well, if he wants to stay, let us leave him here and sail away without him.'

Yet when they told him, Maeldun would not hear of it. 'We set out on this voyage together,' he said. 'We shall finish it together. I will go with you, my friends.'

But because he well knew that the queen would never consent to let him go, he and the others made plans secretly; and on a certain morning, without a word to any of the women, they went down to their ship and made ready to sail. But just as they were putting out from the harbour, the queen came riding down from the fortress carrying a large ball of thread in her hands. Going to the very edge of the water, she flung the ball after the ship, still keeping hold of the end of the thread. Maeldun caught the ball as it came, and it stuck fast to his hand. Then the queen pulled gently on the thread until she had drawn the ship back into harbour again.

'You must not leave me, dear friends,' she said. And so they remained on the island, though unwillingly.

For nine months longer they lived there; and though more than once his comrades persuaded Maeldun to try and sail away, each time the queen came after them and each time she threw the ball of thread, and each time Maeldun caught it, and she drew them back to her.

At last the men blamed Maeldun for their failure to escape. 'He loves the queen too much,' they said. 'He will never leave this island. It is always he, mark you, who catches the ball of thread so that we are re-captured each time.'

Maeldun shrugged his shoulders when he heard this. 'If you blame me for it, then let one of you others catch the ball of thread next time, and see if it does not cling to his hand also.'

The next time they tried to put out to sea and the queen came after them and threw her ball of magic thread, Maeldun stood aside and one of the crew caught the ball of thread and it stuck to his hand, even as it had done to Maeldun's hand.

'Did I not tell you so?' said Maeldun.

The queen immediately began to pull on the thread and draw the ship, as usual, back into harbour. But Diuran quickly took his sword and cut off the man's hand, so that it fell into the sea, still holding the ball of thread. Thereupon the others rowed with all their might out to sea, while the queen and her daughters, on the shore, wept and tore their hair. And thus Maeldun and his companions escaped at last from the island of women.

For many more days they wandered across strange seas, and finally they came to another large island, well wooded to one side, and with a small lake to the other. Here on this pleasant island Maeldun and his crew remained for some days.

One morning, as they were sitting near the lake, they saw an old bird with shabby, tattered feathers bathe itself in the water of the lake. And they saw how, after this bathing, the bird became young and active, with handsome, sleek plumage; and they marvelled at it.

Diuran said eagerly, 'Let us all bathe in the lake, that we may be young for ever.'

But they were afraid and warned him, 'The bird may have left the poison of its old age in the lake. We will not risk touching that water.'

But Diuran was determined, and taking off his clothes, he went into the lake and swam around for a while. Then, after drinking a mouthful of the water, he rejoined his comrades, quite unharmed. None of the others dared follow his example; though they regretted it in after years, for, so long as he lived, Diuran never had a single grey hair, his sight never failed him and he never lost a single tooth; nor did he ever after suffer a day's sickness.

Having victualled their ship from the fruits and the animals on the island, Maeldun and his companions set sail once more, and the next island to which they came seemed, at first sight, a very pleasant one. On it there were many people all laughing and talking amongst each other, and playing at one game or another, continually. It was the turn of Maeldun's youngest foster-brother to go ashore first to see if their reception would be friendly or not; and he set off confidently, for the people seemed good-tempered and kindly. But as soon as he came near to them, he forgot all that had gone before, and he joined in the sport and the laughter of the islanders as though he had lived amongst them for ever.

Maeldun and the others called to him in vain, and waited a long time for him to return to them; but he paid no heed, and they had quite lost sight of him among all the happy folk. So, for fear that none of them might ever see Ireland again if they went after him, they sailed away; and so the king's third son was lost. And though they all mourned for them, no one was really surprised that, of all those who had sailed on the voyage with Maeldun, it should have been his three foster-brothers who were lost, for it had been they who had brought ill luck to the quest by defying the wise man's bidding.

After a few more adventures, they came to a green island where there were cattle and sheep grazing, but no men or women anywhere. They remained a few days in this place and were quite content. But one morning, as a few of them were standing on the top of a hill, a falcon flew by. Instantly two of the men cried out to the others, 'It is a long time since we have seen a falcon like that one. Surely it is a falcon from Ireland?'

Maeldun, looking at the falcon, called, 'Watch carefully in which direction it flies.'

They watched and saw that the falcon flew straight to the south-east, without turning aside.

'There lies Ireland!' they cried; and as one man they ran down to the ship, calling to their comrades, and immediately they all put out to sea and rowed hard for the south-east.

For the rest of that day they rowed, and at dusk they sighted land. 'We are home!' they cried, and made haste towards it. But when they came closer, they found that they had reached, not the coast of Ireland, but only a small island. Downcast and heavy-hearted, they rowed to the shore slowly. Then, as they came nearer and saw a large house standing near the water's edge, they recognized the island for the one where they had overheard the two men quarrelling and had listened to one of them boast how he had slain Ailell of the Edge of Battle.

'It is the raiders' island,' they said. 'We are, after all, close to Ireland.'

'And even closer to revenge,' said Maeldun.

They disembarked silently and walked up the beach to the house. Inside, the raiders were sitting down to their evening meal. Maeldun and his companions, fingering their weapons, stood outside the house in the darkness and listened to what those within were saying.

Presently someone said, 'It is indeed a long time ago that we heard how Maeldun, son of Ailell, had sailed from the mainland in search of us. We have had no sight of him here yet, which is as well for us.'

'Maeldun will never come now,' said another. 'Assuredly, he has been drowned in the great ocean.'

'Do not be so certain of that,' warned another. 'You never can tell, perhaps it will be Maeldun who will wake you up from your night's sleep one fine morning.'

'Supposing that he came here at this very moment,' said another, 'what would we do?'

A voice with authority answered him—it was, indeed, the voice of the leader of the raiders—and Maeldun recognized the voice as that of the man whom he had heard boasting of having killed his father. 'I can tell you what I should do if Maeldun came here tonight. If he still lives, he will have been a long time suffering great hardships; and though we were enemies once, if he were to come to my house I would welcome him kindly, as a friend.'

When Maeldun heard that, he smiled in the darkness and sheathed his sword. Then he went to the door of the house and knocked. When the doorkeeper opened to him and asked his name, he said, 'Tell your master that it is I, Maeldun, son of Ailell of the Edge of Battle, returned safely from my wanderings.'

When the leader of the raiders heard this, he rose quickly from his place and went to the door to greet Maeldun and to bring him and his companions in, to the firelight and the warmth.

All the raiders made them welcome, brought them new garments in place of their travel-stained rags, and set food and drink before them. Long into the night they feasted together in friendship, and Maeldun told the tale of his long wandering, while his new friends marvelled at all they heard and admired the mesh of silver which Diuran had cut from the net at the great pillar.

And so, as he had intended, in the house of his enemies Maeldun's long voyage ended—yet not at all in the manner in which he had expected it to end.

★   ★   ★

At the end of an early manuscript of this story we are told the name of the storyteller: Aed the Fair-haired set down this story as it stands here, that it might be a delight to the mind, and for the people of Ireland who come after him.

9

THE DREAM OF RHONABWY

In this tale a mediaeval Welsh storyteller of the thirteenth or early fourteenth century looks back regretfully at Britain's glorious past and the great ones who are gone. Here King Arthur is not the warrior king with his court of wonder-working heroes who obtained the bride-price for Olwen. But nor is he yet quite Malory's chivalrous fifteenth-century knight; even though amongst Arthur's companions in the dream we do meet several familiar figures who later reappear, somewhat changed, in the pages of Malory: Uwaine, son of King Uriens of Gore and Morgan le Fay; King Mark of Cornwall, the husband of Iseult; and, of course, Sir Kay.

The Dream of Rhonabwy is a more sophisticated story than the others in this book. The writer has deliberately and skilfully contrasted the matter-of-factness of the beginning, and its very everyday happenings, with the vivid, brilliant colours and otherworld atmosphere of the dream. But for all his literary craft and his sophistication, he has woven into his story an extremely ancient element: the mysterious ravens of Owein, who appear here and there in old Welsh literature, and about whom scholars wonder and surmise.

In this story, as at the end of the tale of Oisin, we are reminded how small and insignificant the men of later years considered themselves in comparison with the tall warriors of old; one aspect, no doubt, of the always recurring, nostalgic complaint heard all down the ages about the passing of 'the good old days'.

Madoc ap Maredudd and Iorwerth ap Maredudd were both real historical persons of the twelfth century, sons of the lord of Powys. Madoc died in 1159 and his brother in about 1165.

★　　★　　★

Many hundreds of years ago there ruled in Powys, in Wales, a lord named Madoc. Now Madoc had a brother, Iorwerth, who was ill content that it should be Madoc, and not he, who ruled in Powys.

And though Madoc offered him riches and honours, Iorwerth would have none of his brother's gifts, but instead went raiding into England, plundering, slaying and burning. This was displeasing to Madoc, who wished for peace with England, so he sent men to seek out his brother and forbid him to attack the English. Among those who set forth on this mission was a little band of three, of which the leader was a young man named Rhonabwy.

In the course of their wanderings Rhonabwy came, with his companions, late one evening to the house of one Heilyn the Red. As they approached, they saw the house to be black and old, with a steep gable and smoke pouring through the smoke-hole in the roof. It looked a mean home, and cheerless, and likely to offer them little comfort; but since night was drawing near and the weather looked none too promising, they decided to make the best of what Heilyn had to offer.

Inside, the house was even worse than they had feared. The cattle shared the hall with Heilyn and his family, and the uneven floor of trodden earth was ankle-deep in mire, while great boughs of holly from which the cattle had eaten all the leaves lay everywhere to trip up the unwary in the dim light.

Disgustedly, Rhonabwy and his companions picked their way, slipping and splashing, to the upper end of the hall; and there they found it little better. To one side sat an old hag over a small fire, and to the other, there was nothing but a yellow cowhide spread over the bare boards of the dais. Unwelcomed, the three men sat down near the fire and asked the hag where the master of the house might be. She muttered and mumbled at them, but gave them no reply, and only continued to build up her fire, throwing upon it handfuls of chaff from a heap in her lap and causing such a thick and evil-smelling smoke to fill the hall that Rhonabwy and his companions felt themselves likely to choke from it.

After a time an ill-favoured, red-faced man and a skinny woman came in, he with a bundle of faggots on his back and she with a bundle of faggots under her arm. With barely a greeting to their guests, they flung their wood on the fire; and then the woman fetched stale barley bread, a little cheese and a pitcher of milk and water, and gave them to Rhonabwy and the others in silence.

The three of them would have been quite ready to have gone on and found better lodging for the night, but at that moment the wind blew up, shaking and creaking the old walls of the house, and the rain poured down, dripping through the smoke-hole and making the fire spit and hiss; and they felt that any lodging would be better than to be outside on such an evening. After they had eaten, the old man showed them where they were to sleep—and it was a far from inviting bed, being no more than a heap of dirty straw covered with a threadbare red blanket and a torn, coarse sheet. There was one poorly stuffed pillow, and over the top of all the rest was thrown a dirty coverlet. And worse, they had not been lying down for above half a minute before the fleas hopped out of the straw and started to bite them. Scratching and cursing, Rhonabwy's two companions fell asleep at last; but Rhonabwy himself tossed and turned, unable to rest. He remembered the cowhide spread on the dais and thought, 'Even if it is no more than bare boards under a hide, and nothing over me but my own cloak, it will be better than being eaten alive by fleas,' and he got up and went across to the cowhide and laid himself down on it, fully expecting, tired though he was, to lie there wakeful for hours.

But, little though he knew it, the yellow cowhide was no ordinary one, and the minute he lay down upon it, he fell into a deep sleep; and the minute he was asleep, he started to dream—and he had such a dream as no one had ever had before.

He dreamt that, with his two companions, he was riding across a plain towards the River Severn, and as they rode, they heard a great noise of hooves behind them; and looking round, they saw coming after them a tall, handsome, yellow-haired youth, his beard freshly trimmed and his garments of the finest silk, green and yellow, and his sword gold-hilted. His horse was a chestnut with four white legs and fine trappings of yellow and green. And the green worn by the rider and his horse was as green as the branches of a fir tree, and the yellow as bright as the flowers of the broom. But so fierce was the appearance of this young man, that the three companions took fright and rode on as fast as they could.

And then, in Rhonabwy's dream, a fearsome thing happened, for when the chestnut horse snorted out its breath, the three men were blown far along the highway before it; but when it breathed in, they were dragged back with its breath, right up to their pursuer. So that, in

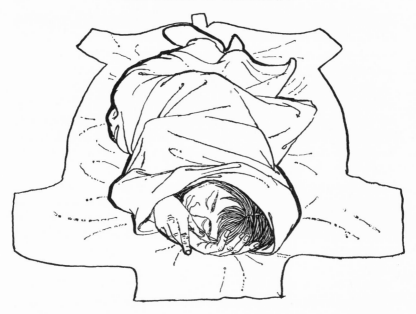

a very little time, they were captured and begged quarter of the yellow-haired youth.

'You have nothing to fear from me,' said the young man. 'You shall have quarter.'

They thanked him, and Rhonabwy said, 'Lord, since you have spared us, tell us your name.'

'There is no reason why I should hide it. I am Iddawg, son of Mynyo.'

Then Rhonabwy and his companions were aware of a great noise of hooves behind them, far greater than that which they had heard before; and looking back, they saw another horseman riding fast towards them. This rider was a tall youth with reddish hair, mounted on a bay horse. He was clad all in red and yellow silk, and the trappings of his horse were red and yellow. And the yellow worn by the rider and his horse was as bright as the flowers of the broom, and the red was as red as blood.

'Iddawg,' the youth called out, 'give me a share of those little men whom you have captured.'

'You shall have a share of them,' replied Iddawg, 'but it shall be a share in offering them friendship, as I have done.'

At that the rider on the bay horse galloped on, and Rhonabwy asked in wonder, 'Who was that, Iddawg?'

'That was Rhyvawn Pebyr, whose father is a great prince.'

Then the four of them rode on as far as the River Severn, and there, before the ford across the river, they found a mighty camp with pavilions and men-at-arms, and on an island below the ford, there was King Arthur, with a bishop to one side of him and a warrior to the other.

Iddawg and Rhonabwy and his two companions came before Arthur and greeted him, and he greeted them in return, looking down at the three strangers. 'Where in all the world, Iddawg, did you find these little men?' he asked.

'I found them yonder, on the road, lord.'

Still looking at them Arthur gave a smile, not altogether of amusement.

'Lord,' asked Iddawg, 'why do you laugh?'

'I do not laugh, Iddawg. Indeed, it saddens me to know that in these later days Britain should be guarded by such little men, so unlike the tall heroes who guarded this land of old.' Then Arthur turned away to speak with the bishop and his counsellors, and Iddawg said to Rhonabwy, 'Did you see the ring with the stone in it, that King Arthur wears on his hand?'

'I did,' replied Rhonabwy.

'Then you will remember all those things which you see here today, for such is the property of that stone in the ring. Had you not seen it, you would have forgotten them.'

At that moment a troop of horsemen reached the ford. Fine men they were, and mounted on fine horses, and all clad in red, the colour of blood. Their tall, proud helmets shone in the sun, so that each man resembled a pillar of red fire.

'Who are they?' asked Rhonabwy admiringly.

'They are the comrades of Rhyvawn Pebyr, whom you saw on the plain. They are served honourably with ale and mead, and theirs is the right to woo the daughters of the lords of Britain,' said Iddawg.

Then up rose one of Arthur's counsellors to ask if they should not proceed against the enemy, Osla of the Big Knife, whom they had

vowed to meet by midday; and Arthur gave the word and the great
host moved forward, each troop in order, across the ford. Iddawg took
Rhonabwy up behind him on the chestnut horse; and when they were
halfway across the river, he turned his horse's head and looked back;
and Rhonabwy saw how there were two other troops coming after
them. The warriors of one troop wore white with black fringes and
black borders to their garments and they carried white banners; and the
other troop wore black, with trimmings of white.

'Who are those warriors, Iddawg?' asked Rhonabwy.

'Those who wear white are the men of Norway, led by March, the
cousin of King Arthur. And those who wear black are the men of Den-
mark, and they have Edern, son of Nudd, to lead them.'

Then Iddawg rode on, while Rhonabwy marvelled at all he saw.
Below Caer Faddon the great host came to rest, and watching, Rhonabwy saw what seemed to him a great confusion in a part of the army
close by, men and horses turning and moving hurriedly as a tall warrior
rode up on a huge horse. The rings of the mail worn by this warrior
were whiter than the whitest lily, and its rivets were redder than the
reddest blood.

'Iddawg,' exclaimed Rhonabwy, 'is the army fleeing?'

'Arthur has never yet fled,' replied Iddawg sternly. 'And if any man
save I had heard those words of yours, you would have died for them.
The men do but hasten to catch sight of Kei, he in the white armour
whom you can see riding yonder. For Kei is handsome above all
others, and the finest horseman in Arthur's court.'

Then someone called out for the earl of Cornwall, and Rhonabwy
saw a fine, tall man arise, holding aloft the sword of Arthur. Upon the
sword was the likeness of two serpents of gold, and when it was drawn
from its scabbard, it was as though two flames of fire came from the
mouths of the serpents.

'It is the duty of the earl of Cornwall,' said Iddawg to Rhonabwy,
'to arm the king in time of battle.'

After that, someone called for Arthur's servant Eiryn, and he rode up
on a sorrel horse with a huge pack strapped on behind him. Eiryn was
a big, ugly man, with red hair and whiskers. He dismounted, and un-
fastening the pack, took out a golden throne and a square rug of silk
with a golden apple at each corner. He spread out this rug before

King Arthur and set the throne upon it, and Arthur sat down on the golden throne, which was big enough for three men sitting side by side.

Then Arthur looked at Owein, son of Urien, who stood near by. 'Owein, will you play chess with me?'

'I will, lord,' replied Owein; and he sat down upon a stool while Eiryn fetched a silver board and chessmen of gold. Then Arthur and Owein began to play.

While they played, Rhonabwy looked about him, and he noticed, a short way off, a white and red pavilion surmounted by the image of a black serpent with shining red eyes and a fiery red tongue. Out of this pavilion now came a young squire with blue eyes and yellow hair, clad finely in yellow silk and bearing a gold-hilted sword in a scabbard of black leather. This youth came near to Owein and greeted him. Owein, startled that the king should not have been greeted first, looked sidelong at Arthur, who said, as though he had guessed Owein's thoughts, 'Bid the youth speak, Owein, his errand is with you.'

Owein turned to the squire, who said to him, 'Lord, is it by your leave that the king's squires and pages are teasing and tormenting your ravens? If it is not, then ask the king to forbid them.'

Owein turned again to Arthur. 'Lord, you have heard what my squire has said. If it please you, order your followers to let my ravens be.'

But Arthur made as though he had not even heard him speak. He gestured with one hand towards the silver board. 'It is your move,' he said.

The young squire returned to his pavilion; but a little while after, as Arthur and Owein were starting a second game, out from a yellow pavilion which was surmounted by the image of a red lion there came a young man with auburn hair and a neatly trimmed beard, wearing garments of yellow silk embroidered with red. In his hands he carried a long sword in a scabbard of red leather. He saluted Owein, who glanced again at Arthur; but, as before, Arthur seemed no whit perturbed by this discourtesy.

'Lord,' said the auburn-haired young man to Owein, 'is it not against your will that the king's followers are attacking and killing your ravens? And if it is against your will, why do you not ask the king to forbid it?'

Owein turned to Arthur. 'Lord, if it please you, forbid your men to harm my ravens.'

As before, Arthur paid no heed to his appeal. 'It is your move,' he said.

The young man returned to the yellow pavilion; and after a while, when Arthur and Owein had finished their second game and started on another, out of a yellow-speckled pavilion which stood some distance away, and was surmounted by the figure of an eagle all in gold, with a jewel in its head, a handsome yellow-haired youth clad in blue silk, who bore a newly sharpened spear with a banner on it, came hurrying towards them, his eyes flashing angrily. He did not wait but greeted Owein and said without ceremony, 'Lord, many of your ravens have been killed, and others lie so crushed and wounded on the ground that they are hardly able to raise their wings from the earth.'

'Lord,' said Owein to Arthur, 'I beg you, call off your men.'

'Owein,' said Arthur, 'it is your move.'

'Go,' said Owein to the youth, 'raise up the banner where the fight is thickest, and let come of it what may.'

The youth ran off to where the ravens fought hardest against Arthur's followers, and there he raised up the banner high above his head; and when they saw it, Owein's ravens took heart and cast off their weariness and flew upwards with a mighty croaking and flapping of their black wings. Then down they dropped upon the heads of Arthur's men, pecking and rending and tearing off limbs. So that, what with the harsh croaking of the ravens and the cries of the wounded men, there arose a great tumult.

Then out from the strife there came riding towards Arthur and Owein a warrior on a dun-coloured horse with trappings of red and yellow. He wore a helmet surmounted by a fearsome leopard's head of gold, with two rubies for its eyes; and on the spear in his hand were broken ravens' feathers.

Weary and troubled, this warrior greeted Arthur. 'Lord, Owein's ravens are slaying your squires.'

Arthur looked at Owein. 'Forbid your ravens to slay my men,' he ordered.

'Lord,' said Owein, as though he had not heard, 'it is your move.'

Arthur moved a chessman, and the warrior rode back to the battle.

After a while there was an even greater noise than before, shouting and wailing and croaking, as Owein's ravens snatched up Arthur's men and tore them to pieces in the air, letting them fall bit by bit to the ground.

Then a young warrior on a grey horse rode hurriedly towards Arthur and Owein as they played. The armour of this warrior was blue, his surcoat was yellow, and he wore a golden helmet set with sapphires and surmounted by a golden lion's head with red eyes. In his hands was a spear which was red with the blood of the ravens; and as he came nearer, it was to be seen that he was Rhyvawn Pebyr.

'Lord,' said he to Arthur, 'do you care nothing for the slaying of your pages, your squires and all your young followers? Without them it will be hard to defend Britain in the years to come.'

'Owein,' commanded Arthur, 'forbid your ravens to kill my men.'

'Lord,' said Owein, 'let us finish this game.'

They finished the game and started another; and as they were nearing the end of that game, there was a greater tumult than ever from the place where the battle raged, ravens croaking and beating their wings, and men crying out and horses neighing, as the ravens tore horse and rider and, lifting them high into the air, dropped them to the ground.

Then with great haste there came towards Arthur and Owein a warrior on a piebald horse, wearing a helmet set with crystals and surmounted by the figure of a griffin, and carrying a spear with a blue-enamelled shaft, its head dripping blood.

'Lord,' he cried out to Arthur, 'the ravens have slain all the men of your household and they have slain all the young sons of the lords of your land, and there will be a day when there is no one left to defend the land of Britain.'

In a great rage, Arthur took up the chessmen from the board, and in his wrath he crushed them in his hands to golden dust. 'Forbid your ravens to kill my men,' he shouted at Owein.

Owein ordered his banner to be lowered; and immediately it had been done, all was peace once more.

Then there came four and twenty warriors from Osla of the Big Knife to ask Arthur for a truce for a month and a half; and after Arthur had sought counsel of his bishop and of Kei, of his cousin

March and of Rhyvawn Pebyr, and of many others, he granted the truce.

Then Kei called out that camp should be struck. 'Let every man who wishes to follow our lord King Arthur make ready to ride with him to Cornwall,' he cried. And immediately there was a confusion of sound, such as had never been heard before; men calling out, horses neighing, armour clanking, weapons clashing, as the great host made ready to move on. And with this noise Rhonabwy awoke and found himself lying on the yellow cowhide in the house of Heilyn, having slept for three nights and three days. And because he had woken before he had asked Iddawg the meaning of the battle between Arthur's young men and Owein's ravens, no one knows the meaning to this day.

A NOTE ON THE PRONUNCIATION

GAELIC

For the Gaelic names in this book, I have chosen that spelling, anglicized or otherwise, which I considered the most convenient. Approximate pronunciations—which are quite near enough for general purposes—are given for all the difficult Gaelic names in the *List of Names* at the end of the book. Any Gaelic name which does not appear in this list may be pronounced as though it were English.

WELSH

The pronunciation of Welsh is far less difficult than it appears at first sight. All the important Welsh names occurring in the stories are given with their pronunciations in the *List of Names;* but in order to save the reader from having to refer too often to this list while reading, the following notes may be found helpful as a rough indication of the approximate pronunciation of Southern Welsh:

Vowels

A   long as in *palm*, short as in *cat*
E   long as *a* in *late*, short as in *get*
I, U, Y   long as *i* in *machine*, short as *i* in *bit*
W   when used as a vowel: long as *oo* in *cool*, short as *oo* in *wood*

Diphthongs

AE, AI, EI, EU, EY   as the English word *eye*
AW   as *ow* in *cow*
EW   as *oo* in *cool*

Consonants

C   always hard as in *cat*
CH   as in Scottish *loch*
DD   as *th* in *this*

F   as English *v*
G   always hard as in *go*
LL   approximately as *l* preceded by *h, hl*
TH   always as in *thin*

Any letters not mentioned above may be pronounced as in English.
Welsh words are usually stressed on the last syllable but one.

LIST OF NAMES

Key to the Pronunciation

aw as in *lawn*
ay as in *day*
ah as the sound of *a* in *father*
air as in *pair*
ă as in *comma* rather than as in *hat*
ee as in *see*
ĕ as in *red*
er as in *pert*
ī as in *time*
ĭ as in *ship*
ō as in *robe*
ŏ as in *dog*
o͞o as in *gloom*
o͝o as in *good*
ow as in *now*
TH as in *that*
th as in *thing*
g as in *get*
H is used to indicate the sound of *ch* as in the Scottish *loch* or German *ich*

Stressed syllables are shown by a stress mark (') placed after the syllable which is stressed.

Aed (ayd)
Aes Sidhe (ays shee)
Aethlem (īth'lĕm)
Aev (ayv)
Ailell (ăl'yĕl)
Aned (ăn'ĕd)
Arianrod (ă-rĭ-ăn'rŏd)
Avarta (ăv'ahr-tă)

Bedwyr (bĕd'weer)
Beli (bĕl'ĭ)
Bilé (bĭl'ay)
Boann (bō'ăn)
Bov (bōv)
Bran, son of Llyr (brahn)
Bran, Finn's hound (brăn)
Branwen (brăn'wĕn)

Brigit (brĭg'ĭt)
Brugh (brōōH)
Cado (kăd'ō)
Canhastyr (kăn-hăs'teer)
Caswallawn (kăs-wă'hlown)
Creidylad (krī-dĭl'ăd)
Custennin (kĭs-tĕn'nĭn)
Cwm Cawlwyd (kōōm kowl'-
    wĭd)
Dana (dah'nă)
Dara (dah'ră)
Dillus (dĭ'hlĭss)
Diuran (dyōōr'ăn)
Diurnach (dyōōr'nahH)
Don (dōn)
Drudwyn (drĭd'wĭn)
Edern (ĕd'airn)
Eidoel (ī'doyl)
Eiryn (ī'rĭn)
Eochai Airem (yō'Hay ă'rĕm)
Etain (ĕt'ayn)
Etar (ĕt'ahr)
Eurei (ī'rī)
Fatha (fah'hă)
Feradach (fĕ'ră-dahH)
Fiachna (fee'ăH-nă)
Fiachra (fee'ăH-ră)
Fianna (fee'ăn-nă)
Finn Ban Mac Bresal (fĭn bahn
    măk brĕss'ăl)
Fuamnach (fōōm'nahH)
Gawlgawd (gowl'gowd)
geis (gaysh)
Germaun (ger'mawn)
Gilla Dacker (gĭl'lă dăk'er)
Glini (glĭn'ĭ)
Goreu (gaw'rĭ)

Greidawl (grī'dowl)
Grugyn (grĭg'ĭn)
Gwalchmei (gwahlH'mī)
Gwawl (gwowl)
Gweddu (gwĕTH'ĭ)
Gwern Abwy (gwairn ăb'wee)
Gwrhyr (gōōr'eer)
Gwrnach (gōōr'năH)
Gwyddno (gwĭTH'nō)
Gwydion (gwĭd'yŏn)
Gwyn (gwĭn)
Gwythyr (gwĭth'eer)
Heilyn (hī'lĭn)
Iddawg (ee'THowg)
Iorwerth (yawr'wairth)
Kei (kī)
Kicva (kĭk'vă)
Kilcoed (kĭl'coyd')
Kilgwri (kĭl-gōō'rĭ)
Kilhwch (kĭl'hōōH)
Kilydd (kĭl'ĭTH)
Kironn (keer'ŏn)
Kynddelig (kĭn-THĕl'ĭg)
Liagan (lee'ă-găn)
Lir (leer)
Llamrei (hlăm'rī)
Lleu Llaw Gyffes (hlī hlow gĭf'-
    fĕss)
Lludd (hleeTH)
Lwyd (hlōō'ĭd)
Llwydawg (hlōō-ĭd'owg)
Llwyr (hlōō'eer)
Llyn Llyw (hlĭn hlee'ōō)
Llyr (hleer)
Lochlann (lŏH'lăn)
Mabon (măb'ŏn)
Madoc (măd'ŏk)

Maeldun (mayl′dōōn)
Manannan Mac Lir (măn′ăn-ăn
   măk leer)
Manawyddan (măn-ă-wĭTH′ăn)
Maredudd (mă-rĕd′ĭTH)
Matholwch (măth-ŏl′ōōH)
Menw (mĕn′ōō)
Midir (mĭd′eer)
Mioch (mee′ŏH)
Modron (mŏd′rŏn)
Mynyo (mĭn′yō)
Niav (nee′ahv)
Nuada (nōō′ă-THă)
Nudd (neeTH)
Oisin (ŏsh′een)
Olwen (ŏl′wĕn)

Owein (ō′wĭn)
Pryderi (prĭ-day′rĭ)
Pwyll (pwĭl)
Redynvre (rĕd-ĭn′vray)
Rhiannon (ree-ăn′nŏn)
Rhonabwy (rŏn-ăb′wee)
Rhymi (ree′mĭ)
Rhyvawn   Pebyr   (ree′vown
   pĕb′eer)
Sav (sahv)
sidhe (shee)
Skolaun (skō′lawn)
Taliesin (tăl-ĭ-ay′sĭn)
Teirtu (tīr′tĭ)
Trwyth (trōō′ĭth)